CANCER, COCAINE AND COURAGE

The Story of Dr. William Halsted

Born: September 23, 1852
Died: September 7, 1922

Books by Arthur J. Beckhard

CANCER, COCAINE AND COURAGE
The Story of Dr. William Halsted
(with William D. Crane)

ELECTRICAL GENIUS: Nikola Tesla

BLACK HAWK

Cancer, Cocaine and Courage

The Story of Dr. William Halsted

by
Arthur J. Beckhard
and
William D. Crane

Julian Messner, Inc.   New York

Published by Julian Messner, Inc.
8 West 40 Street, New York 18

Published simultaneously in Canada
by The Copp Clark Publishing Co. Limited

© Copyright 1960 by Arthur J. Beckhard

Printed in the United States of America

Library of Congress Catalog Card No. 60–13268

To Esther and Peg

ACKNOWLEDGMENT

The authors most gratefully acknowledge the gracious co-operation of Mrs. Theodore Savage, Mrs. A. A. Stokes, and Mr. William Halsted Vander Poel in helping to gather personal material concerning Dr. William Stewart Halsted. Our thanks go also to Dr. Arthur Neergaard and Dr. Robert Cushing for so generously giving of their time for consultation on medical matters, and to Mr. Thomas P. Fleming, librarian of the College of Physicians and Surgeons, Juliet R. Kellogg, associate archivist of Phillips Academy, and Susan Young Crawford, research abstractor for the American Medical Association, for their patient and helpful correspondence. We are also greatly indebted to the members of the staff of the New York Academy of Medicine who were always most courteous and co-operative.

Chapter

I

HEAVY FOOTSTEPS SOUNDED MENACINGLY ON THE THICK WOOD cellar steps. The boy bending over the low worktable did not hear them. Beads of perspiration glistened on his forehead. His tongue, clenched between his teeth, protruded from his lips. His hand shook as he touched the gleaming razor to the white skin of the upturned belly of the frog pinioned on a piece of white wrapping paper on the table in front of him. Although the frog was dead, the boy was surprised to discover that it took courage to make that first incision.

The descending footsteps made the open flame quiver in the glass bowl of the gas fixture on the wall above him, and the boy frowned. But now the deed was done. He laid the razor down and began carefully peeling back the thin skin.

"William!"

The boy turned quickly to face the storm that he knew was coming.

"Yes, Father."

"What do you mean by sneaking off and hiding down here in the cellar on a bright, sunshiny day?"

"I didn't sneak off. I just came down here. Anybody could have seen me."

William Halsted, Sr. glared at his son, first in exasperation, then in anger. Young William returned his father's stare fearlessly but without impertinence. Had a stranger happened to glance through the low cellar window on that sunlit morning in 1862, he would have guessed that the stocky, bearded man, and the stocky, square-faced boy were father and son. Obviously they were fond of each other, yet stubbornly opposed.

"What is my best Napoleon brandy doing here? Don't tell me—"

"I wasn't drinking it. I used it to clean the instrument. It says in the book the scalpel should be cleaned in alcohol and—"

"Book! Instrument! Scalpel! What are you talking about? What are you doing?"

"I was operating on a frog, Father," young William answered steadily.

"Operating on a frog!" Mr. Halsted brushed the boy aside and looked down at the worktable. A quick glance sufficed. He turned to his son, his face suddenly purple with shock and anger.

"How dare you?" he asked hoarsely. "How dare you?"

"I only used a few drops of the brandy, Father. Honest, I—"

"I'm not referring to the use of my best brandy. Nor do I more than mention your using my razor—"

"It's your Friday razor, Father. Today's Tuesday. I knew you wouldn't be needing—"

"How dare you defy God? That's what I'm talking about. Not the razor and the brandy—those are things I can punish you for. But how dare you— Have you no fear? No reverence?"

"I don't understand, Father. Of course I—"

"Haven't you been taught to recognize God's prerogatives? Don't we go to church three times in every week?

Haven't you learned in all this time that God alone has the right to know what his creatures look like inside as well as out?"

"No, I didn't know that. I thought—"

"Whatever made you think of doing such a dreadful thing?"

"There's a book in Uncle Thad's house. It's got pictures and diagrams. I wanted to see if I could find the same lines that—"

"So it's your Uncle Thaddeus' influence that's turning my son into a heathen—performing black magic in the cellar. Well, I can do something about— Look!"

Suddenly Mr. Halsted pointed a trembling finger at the frog on the worktable.

"Look! It moved! It's still alive! You were cutting—"

"He's not alive, Father. He was dead when I found him. That's just what the book calls reflex action."

"You reflex-action yourself right up to your room, young man. I'll speak to your uncle Thaddeus! And to your mother! We'll see that this sort of thing is stopped! Will you promise to stay in your room or must I lock you in?"

"I'll stay."

"Wait! Before you go, you'd best wrap that—that thing up and throw it in the furnace. I'll take charge of the brandy and my razor."

More than an hour later the family conclave was still in full session in the walnut-paneled second-story living room of the Halsted summer house at Irvington, New York. Mr. Halsted, his hands clasped behind his frock-coated back, his neatly trimmed, spade-shaped beard sunk on his chest, paced the room more in sorrow than in anger. Mrs. Halsted, knowing from long years of experience and many similar scenes, that it was best to allow the storm to blow itself out, sat in a high-backed wing chair, apparently concentrating on her crocheting.

Once in a while a little smile appeared at the corners of her mouth. A smile also twisted the thin lips of Dr. Thaddeus Halsted, but his was not a pleasant smile to see. A tall, gaunt man, he stood by the deep-set Dutch window staring out at the rock garden and shade trees of the Halsted estate, but seeing something very different. He seemed strangely out of place in that dark, formal room. His dusty boots, his worn blue uniform of the United States Medical Service were in marked contrast to the gleaming parquet floor and the precise symmetry with which the heavy furniture had been arranged.

"Don't you think you are making a good deal too much fuss over nothing?" Thaddeus Halsted asked. Mrs. Halsted frowned and shook her head at him, but it was too late. The damage had been done.

"Nothing! Is that what you said? Nothing?" William Halsted shouted. "I daresay it *would* seem like that to you!"

"It not only would; it does," his brother replied. "After all, the boy has not committed a crime. He hasn't killed anyone. He hasn't burned the house down. He hasn't contracted some unmentionable disease—"

"Thaddeus!" thundered the angry father.

"He's not quite eleven, Thaddeus," Mrs. Halsted said demurely.

Thaddeus grinned at her. She had a way of always being able to take the bitterness out of his words—of making him feel foolish, as if he were behaving like an overgrown bully. For years she had been the peacemaker between these two dissimilar brothers.

"Don't think that being a doctor gives you the right to speak of clinical matters in my wife's presence! If it hadn't been for you and your irreligious book, the boy would not have dreamed of invading God's province."

"I'll not argue with you, William. We've been over all this so many times! You know I believe that God does not frown on those who try to help heal the sick."

"And you are equally aware of my belief that faith cures all ills. To think of my son opening the body of one of God's creatures is revolting. How could he? A son of mine! Where would he get so vile an idea?"

William Halsted glared fiercely at his brother, then turned to his wife.

"Don't look accusingly at me, William," she said, smiling sweetly. "Don't forget that my father, Richard Townley Haines, was co-founder with your father of the Union Theological Seminary!"

"I wasn't looking at you accusingly. I was merely expressing wonder that a son of ours should show such impious tendencies."

"Impious!" It was Thaddeus' turn to explode. "How any man in his right mind can consider an anatomy book impious is beyond me!"

"All those drawings of the insides of men and women!" Mr. Halsted continued, ignoring his brother's interruption. "It's not only an invasion of God's sole right to know and understand the inner workings of man; it's also an invasion of human privacy—an insult to human dignity."

"How can anyone look at those infinitely complicated tracings of nerves and veins and fail to realize the greatness of a power that could create them? There's nothing impious or profane about the book, William."

"I want you to lock up that book, Thaddeus. Think of it! My daughter Minnie might have seen it! She's at an impressionable age—just blooming into young womanhood."

"Oh, William!" Mrs. Halsted protested.

"Granted your children are precocious, Brother William," Thaddeus said, grinning impishly. "But surely, at eight, Minnie—"

"And there's Richard," Mr. Halsted said quickly. "Certainly you won't deny that there's no one with more curiosity than a six-year-old."

"And Bertha! What of her?" Thaddeus exclaimed in mock horror. "At four, one is so easily led astray."

"I tell you I will not have my children corrupted," Mr. Halsted continued, ignoring the interruption.

"The only organ they know about is the one in the church," Thaddeus said. "Not the human organs—the heart, the lungs—"

"I repeat," Mr. Halsted interrupted. "It is not for mere men to pry into God's domain. It is impious."

"Then you consider that you were impious, profane, and unhealthy when you were young Will's age," Thaddeus interrupted.

"I? Certainly not! I should never have been allowed to—"

"Then I, as your elder brother, was gravely in error. I always thought—when you used to take the dictionary to bed with you—that you did it in order to satisfy a natural curiosity, although I never for one moment considered the possibility of your merely trying to increase your vocabulary."

William Halsted stared at his older brother in shocked amazement, his face turning from red to maroon. Mrs. Halsted's face was almost as red as she tried vainly to stifle the laugh that burst gaily from her lips. Mr. Halsted looked from his brother to his laughing wife, then suddenly threw back his head and roared with laughter that made hers seem like a chuckle in comparison. Quickly she arose and went to her husband.

"Oh, William," she said in a choked voice, "I do love you."

Her amazed husband looked over her blond curls at his brother. He had not the slightest idea whether his wife's voice was choked by laughter or by tears.

"Whenever you are about to become your most pompous, you save the day by laughing at yourself, William. I have a confession to make. I too have peeked into the pages of that book!"

"You didn't!"

"I did. I found nothing particularly shocking."

"You didn't?"

"No, I didn't. I'm a big girl now, William, and I'm afraid that I wasn't too surprised by anything I saw—except that I was surprised to see how unattractive ladies and gentlemen can be without their skins."

"These modern women!" William Halsted sighed. "A man has no defense against them. No man is respected in his own home any longer!"

He smiled as he spoke, and gave his wife's waist a little squeeze.

"This middle-aged romancing is all very well," Thaddeus said, grinning at them, "but what's to be done with your evil-minded son?"

"You run up and tell him I've decided to forgive him, Thaddeus," William said.

"Forgive him for what?" his brother asked relentlessly.

"I know!" Mrs. Halsted exclaimed delightedly. "You can forgive him for taking your razor."

Her husband nodded eagerly. "But mind, Thaddeus. You must insist that he never do such a thing again. I don't like to think of his handling that sharp blade."

"Oh, I'll be very firm," Thaddeus promised.

"You'll tell him there's to be no more nonsense with that book?"

"No, but I'll do better. I'll keep the book out of reach."

"No encouraging him to follow in your footsteps, now."

"Don't worry, William. I would never encourage anyone I care for to become a doctor."

"Well, I must say I never expected *you* to say a thing like that."

"We've not talked much since I returned. It will be many years before time can erase the shame that has befallen my profession. So, you see, you have no cause to fear. I shall not urge your son to waste his life as I have wasted mine."

Without waiting for a reply, Thaddeus Halsted opened the heavy oak door and disappeared in the dark shadows of the long hallway.

Young William Stewart Halsted stood at the window of his bedroom watching the sun disappear. Just below his room was the formal garden, then two long greenhouses, side by side, their glass roofs turned into gleaming gold by the rays of the setting sun. He was hungry but not unduly alarmed by the prospect of going to bed without supper. He was pretty sure that his mother would somehow manage to have his German governess smuggle food to him. Funny how much better a glass of milk tasted when it was handed in with a whispered word of secrecy.

The sun dropped out of sight suddenly—as if someone had given a yank to the far end of a string attached to the big orange balloon. The roofs of the greenhouses were suddenly no longer golden. They had turned a deep slate gray. It was getting late. The footsteps should be heard any time now. There they were! But those were neither Hahnie's nor his mother's steps. Was his father coming up to punish him? He turned to face the door.

"Uncle Thad!"

"None other. Thaddeus Halsted, Esquire, emissary extraordinary on an important mission from the palace. You have been forgiven. You have been reinstated as the rightful heir to the throne. There is, however, one condition."

"What is it, Sir Thaddeus?"

"You are to wash hands, face, ears, and any other exposed parts, and join the royal family in the great dining hall."

"That all?"

"You are to promise to leave your father's razors strictly alone in the future."

"Uncle Thad, the book is wrong. I only had time to take one quick look at the frog's insides, but there weren't any red and blue lines like the ones in the book."

"Of course the book is wrong. All books are wrong. You will do well to forget that they exist."

The boy looked at his tall uncle earnestly for a moment.

"I never know when you're fooling and when you're in earnest," he said.

"Don't give it a thought, boy," Uncle Thaddeus replied. "I seldom know myself." He dropped a friendly hand on his stocky nephew's shoulder. "Now get those hands clean and come along. The ears can wait till bedtime. I'm getting pretty all fired hungry."

"Me too," said young William Stewart Halsted, ungrammatically but with great enthusiasm.

WILL'S MOTHER WAS THE ONLY ONE IN THE FAMILY WHO spoke softly. Both his father and Thaddeus Halsted were inclined to shout at each other, and the boy, without intending to eavesdrop, could not help hearing several of the family conferences.

"The Devil has work for idle hands to do," William Halsted boomed just as Will was passing the closed doors of the living room on his way upstairs. An indistinguishable murmur followed—his uncle remonstrating.

"Don't think I have forgotten the frog incident."

"Oh, William!"

"Well, maybe I should forget it; but I think the boy should be sent away to school."

"For once I agree with your husband." It was his uncle's voice. "It's high time he went with boys of his own age. And he should have some men teachers. D'you realize, Emmy, that the boy's had only you and that old German battle-ax—"

Will clapped his hand over his mouth so his parents wouldn't hear him laughing at his uncle's description of Miss Hahnstein.

"And besides," his father continued, "New York is no place for the children at this time. But I must go back to town.

18

Halsted and Haines just received a large government order
for uniforms, and I must be there to supervise. Coming back
and forth every day would be impossible."

"The wounded from Antietam will be coming back home
now," Thaddeus continued, ignoring both interruptions.
"The streets will be filled with grim processions of the
maimed and their desperately cheerful relatives. Nothing
for children's eyes."

"Couldn't you stay on here with them, Thad? I'd appreciate it if—"

"I should have left last month, William. The shortage of
doctors in New York is so acute that the hospitals are wel-
coming even the halt and the lame and the half-blind."

"You're not well enough, Thaddeus," Mrs. Halsted interrupted.

"I'm as well as I shall ever be," Thaddeus replied. "Once
the Southern swamp fever gets its hooks into a man, it has
a way of not letting go; but I'll be all right, and I'm needed.
Couldn't Will go off to school somewhere, and the others
stay on here? I may make fun of her, but Hahnie is really
very devoted to the youngsters."

"The Irvington school is quite good I hear, and Will can
go to Monson. Mr. Tufts is such a fine little man."

So Will was not surprised to find himself one of some
thirty students when the small private school at Monson,
Massachusetts, opened its fall term a few weeks later. He
found it impossible to share his mother's enthusiasm for the
Reverend Mr. Tufts and his great fondness for Latin and
lengthy sermons. It was Will's first time away from home
and, as he grew more homesick, it seemed to him that Latin
became duller and the sermons longer and the chapel
benches harder every day—until, finally, he felt that he
simply could not face another minute of it. Without any

preconceived plan he simply walked right past the open chapel door, and kept on walking.

The birds seemed to sing louder; the foliage seemed more vivid; the whole countryside seemed more attractive and alive the moment he left the school grounds. The eight miles to Palmer, the nearest town to Monson, seemed to take no time at all. He was pleased to discover that he had enough change in his pocket to buy a ticket to Springfield, and he cheerfully boarded the first eastbound train that pulled in.

In Springfield, the smell wafting across the busy station from a long lunch counter made him realize that he was hungry. Glad that his capital would provide him with milk and a doughnut, he headed in the direction of the enticing odor. But he did not get far.

"Just where do you think you're going, young man?" a deep voice boomed behind him.

Turning quickly, Will saw a big man with enormous mustaches and beetling black eyebrows staring down at him.

"What's your name, boy?"

"William Halsted."

"That's what I thought," the big man said, and thrust a flimsy piece of yellow paper into Will's hand. "Read that. That is, if you can read."

It was addressed to the station master, Springfield, Massachusetts.

BOY ELEVEN MAY BE ON 4:30 EASTBOUND ANSWERS TO NAME HALSTED REQUEST YOU PUT HIM ABOARD FIRST WESTBOUND TRAIN HAVE CONDUCTOR WATCH HIM CLOSELY WILL MEET HIM PALMER STATION.

It was signed REV. PHINEAS TUFTS.

As the train pulled into the Palmer station some two hours

later, Will spotted the school carryall with the Reverend Mr. Tufts seated forbiddingly in the back seat. He got off the train and walked meekly to the big wagon, and optimistically set a foot on the iron step that led to the driver's seat.

"In back here, please," said the Reverend Mr. Phineas Tufts.

Will opened the door and joined his mentor in the back of the vehicle. The driver chirruped to his horses, who began to trot in leisurely syncopation. The silence in the carriage was unbroken.

At last Mr. Tufts spoke, and Will was surprised to notice that his voice broke.

"What will your dear mother think? What will your father say?"

Will had been wondering about the same thing, and the answer was not a pleasant one.

"I suppose I must punish you," the little professor said.

"Yes, sir."

Again silence descended upon the occupants of the carryall, broken by the clop-clop of the team's hooves on the sun-baked road. They had traveled nearly half the distance to the school before Mr. Tufts spoke again.

"It will probably seem to your father that we are abusing you here. Do *you* feel we've treated you badly?"

"No, sir."

"We can ill afford to lose the tuition your father pays, Willie. Costs have gone up dreadfully. Salaries too. We need every penny we can get. Tell me, Willie—that is, if you wouldn't mind—if you don't think you were treated badly, why were you running away? Now's the time to voice your complaints, if you have any."

"Well, sir, the sermons are so long, sir. And the seats are so hard."

It sounded even sillier to Will than he had feared and he was sure Mr. Tufts would laugh. He didn't.

"I'm glad you told me," he said. "P'rhaps I *have* grown to enjoy the sound of my own voice. And the seats—you know, I've never sat on those benches."

"They're mean, sir," Will said earnestly.

"The housekeeper might sew up some kind of cushions for them," Mr. Tufts said thoughtfully. "And perhaps you and some of your friends could collect some hay and help her stuff them. That might be quite a job—"

"I'll do it," Will said quickly.

"Good. And I hope you have learned something from this incident, Willie. We never solve our problems by trying to run away from them. If we stay and face them, we can almost always lick them. Remember that."

"I will, Mr. Tufts."

"In that case I see no need to trouble your father with an account of your escapade, do you?"

"No, sir. I don't think it's necessary at all."

The new relationship with Mr. Tufts, as well as the welcome comfort of the new seat-pads, changed Will's outlook on life at Monson so completely that the term was over before he knew it and he found himself actually looking forward to returning in the fall.

The year 1865 was a time of contrasting emotions. Feelings swung in a great arc from the heights of rejoicing over the end of the Civil War to the depths of shock and grief over the assassination of President Lincoln. Will's mind registered these events. He took part in the parades and the lighting of great bonfires at the time of Lee's surrender and he felt a sense of loss at the death of a man he admired, but it was as if these events were unreal—as if he were living in a vacuum—for his thoughts were concentrated on the fact that he was to enter Andover in the fall.

"Andover, then Yale, and then a place in the business," his father had said. "That's what we have in mind for you, your mother and I. How does it sound to you?"

"It sounds fine, Father. I only hope I can make good all along the line," Will had answered.

He had never been a brilliant student and he knew he would have to sacrifice opportunities to go picnicking and dancing that summer if he were to pass his Andover entrance examinations.

Even after he had taken them, he was not at all sure that he had passed. The weeks that followed were anxious ones and he was greatly relieved when he learned he had just squeaked through. For the moment, at least, he was the family hero. His mother hugged him; the younger children gazed upon him admiringly. His father pretended to take the whole thing as a matter of course but could not quite succeed in hiding his satisfaction. Only Uncle Thaddeus held himself somewhat aloof. It seemed to Will almost as if his uncle were an observer, rather than a participant, in the family's happiness. Will was both puzzled and hurt and after a few days managed to summon the courage to question his uncle.

"Aren't you pleased about my going to Andover, Uncle Thad?" he asked.

"Pleased? Of course I'm pleased. You are, aren't you?"

"Oh, yes. I think I'm pretty lucky."

"Luckier than you know, I think," Thaddeus said, smiling a little wryly. "You're not bothered by doubts at all, are you?"

"Doubts?"

"I mean you don't object to your life being planned for you?"

Will grinned cheerfully. "It's like being one of the royal family," he said.

Thaddeus allowed his arm to drop affectionately across his nephew's shoulders in a quick hug.

"Good," he said, and then, stepping back, eyed Will as he might a patient who had come to him for the first time. "You know, you never *have* had any craving for a career, have you? I mean, most boys have secret plans—"

"Oh, sure. I had them," Will answered, laughing. "When I was little I wanted to be a great scientist. Remember? And then I wanted to be a soldier, and then a policeman or a fireman. And later on I wanted to run a greenhouse."

Uncle Thaddeus smiled. "But never a lawyer or an engineer or an architect?"

Will shook his head.

"Or a doctor?"

"Oh, no!"

Will's denial was so emphatic that his uncle's eyebrows rose questioningly and Will flushed in embarrassment.

"I'm sorry, Uncle Thad. I clean forgot that you—"

"Quite all right, boy. Don't apologize. I like your honesty. But I can't help being curious. Why the emphatic negative?"

"Because—well, because a doctor can't have a life of his own," Will answered reluctantly, feeling, even as he spoke, that he was disappointing the one member of the family to whom he had always felt closest. "A doctor must always be ready to go wherever he's called, whenever somebody thinks he needs him."

"I'm glad you've thought things out," Thaddeus answered. "And I'm relieved too. I'm sure you've decided wisely about your future. And your father will be very happy to have you in the business."

Almost immediately after his arrival at Andover, Will

became aware that the school differed from Monson as markedly as the headmaster contrasted to the timid, somewhat hesitant Reverend Mr. Tufts.

Short, stocky, with a square beard and beetling eyebrows, Dr. Samuel Taylor was barrel-chested and bellicose. In a booming voice he informed all incoming freshmen that Andover Academy was run on a military basis; that strict discipline would be maintained both in and out of class; that all students must be indoors at eight o'clock every night, and woe betide anyone caught breaking the rules.

As Dr. Taylor undoubtedly knew, this introductory speech could not fail to act as a challenge to every new boy's ingenuity; and every freshman left the headmaster's study fully determined to be out after eight o'clock at some time in the near future. However, their high hopes and ambitions were soon dashed. Within the first few days of the semester, upper classmen found occasion to warn each one of them that, though almost everyone had tried, no one had ever been successful. No one knew how "Uncle Sam," as the headmaster was called, managed to achieve this perfect detection. There had been various theories. Years ago most of the boys had thought that gardeners and janitors—even faculty members—had been stationed at strategic points around the campus with spyglasses, but this theory had been discarded when the whereabouts of all personnel had been carefully accounted for. Most boys now held to the belief that Dr. Taylor himself went on the prowl at night, peering into dormitory windows, testing doors, and in other ways accounting for the presence of each and every boy.

Will could scarcely believe that the headmaster of a distinguished institution like Andover Academy would waste his time in snooping, so he tried to put the matter out of his thoughts and concentrate on his studies. Again he was faced with the pitfalls of advanced Latin and mathematics, and found that he had to be indoors by eight if he were to finish his homework for the next day's class. But, when many of his classmates attempted to escape from their boarding-houses or the dormitory after hours, only to be ignomini-ously summoned to "Uncle Sam's" study next day, he de-termined to investigate and find out for himself.

One dark night he slipped out of Mrs. Flagg's boarding-house and made his way up the hill to Dr. Taylor's house. If "Uncle Sam" were doing any prowling he would be doing it about now, Will thought. The double brick house where the headmaster lived was surrounded by a fence and bushes; but the path to the door was clear, and lighted by a street lamp most of the night. Will took up a position across the street where he could watch the house, and waited. He could see a man's head and shoulders silhouetted against the blinds, so he reasoned that "Uncle Sam" was in his study. He watched an hour. Some lights came on in the house; others went out. A few late buggy riders passed his hiding place. Will waited patiently. "Uncle Sam" still sat at his desk. Either the rumors were wrong or this was not "Uncle Sam's" night for hiding behind bushes.

The next day at morning prayers Will smiled to himself. No boys would be punished today. The final prayer was raised to Heaven, and the last "Amen" said with noticeable gusto. Now came the moment feared by all. At this point it was Dr. Taylor's custom to read a list of names with the terse request that they report to his study immediately.

"Will William Halsted please report to my study immedi-ately?"

Will's heart raced. He tried not to see the glances of his classmates or hear their not too kind remarks. In the study, Will sat down in the only possible chair—a very straight one placed in front of Dr. Taylor's desk. From behind this barrier Dr. Taylor eyed him as one might look at a spot of dirt before wiping it out. He saw a rather slight fourteen-year-old boy with noticeably large ears and a long mouth that seemed ready at any moment to break into a grin. Unlike most of the boys who faced him across his desk during these personal interviews, Will showed no apparent timidity. He held his head high, and looked inquiringly at his headmaster without a trace of fear.

"Halsted," Dr. Taylor said as he removed his spectacles and breathed on them thoughtfully, "I understand that your classmates call you the 'Quiet One.' Is that true?"

"I don't know, sir," Will answered, caught by surprise at the unexpected question. "Do they?"

"So I'm told. At any rate, I've perceived at firsthand that you've always been quiet and attentive in my classes."

With a flourish the older man pulled a voluminous white handkerchief from the tail pocket of his Prince Albert coat and began wiping his spectacles.

"I've reason to consider you one of our best-behaved students, Halsted," he continued.

"Thank you, sir," Will answered.

He was puzzled. There was always something a little ominous about "Uncle Sam" when he used his mildest voice. Will wondered if this was the same cat-and-mouse game he had seen him use on others—and at the same moment he noticed a life-sized bust of Beethoven on a pedestal in front of the window. A sudden sense of foreboding engulfed him as he realized that the desk lamp would throw a shadow of the bust on the window blind.

"Halsted," Dr. Taylor said, "I want to ask you a question, and I expect an honest answer. Have you heard rumors that I prowl about the grounds at night spying on the boys?"

"Yes, sir, I have."

"Do you believe them?"

"I—I don't know, sir."

"I can see you hardly approve. You think it would be sneaky. Is that so?"

"Yes, sir."

"Are you taking into account the fact that it is my job to see that rules are obeyed and that Andover turns out boys who develop into fine men?"

"If you trusted us, no one would go out after hours, sir."

"No? I've trusted you. How do you explain the fact that I saw you prowling around my house last night?"

Will's mouth fell open. He tried to speak, but no words came.

"What have you got to say to that?"

The corners of Will's mouth twitched as he suppressed a smile. The opportunity was too good to be passed up, whatever the consequences might be.

"Only, sir"—and the emphasis was on the *sir*—"that you are a far better prowler than I am."

Thunderclouds gathered. Will kept his head high and waited for the storm to break. Suddenly he heard a strange noise, as though Dr. Taylor had swallowed too hard. Then came a chuckle . . . and a laugh, genuine, hearty, and infectious.

"I think we'll get along. You can forget about last night," Dr. Taylor said in a tone of dismissal.

As Will got up to go, Dr. Taylor stopped him.

"About that 'Quiet One' business," he said. "It's all right in class, but it doesn't help very much in making friends. Making friends—learning to get along with other people—is almost as important as your studies. There's a new boy in school. Name's Bush. Served in the war. Good deal older than the rest of you. He's going to organize Andover's first baseball team. Everybody will be starting from scratch,

Halsted. Nobody else will know any more about the game than you do. Why don't you give it a try?"

"I will, sir," Will answered.

"And have you tried?" Thaddeus Halsted asked when Will went home for Christmas vacation, and told him about the prowling incident.

"I haven't had time yet," Will replied. "I've had to bone up on a couple of subjects in order to make time for practice, but I plan to when I go back."

"You'll find there's nothing in the whole world any more exciting than being part of a team," Uncle Thad said. "There are lots of games and sports that don't depend on teamwork. Boxing, fencing, tennis—for instance. I don't mean to say they aren't worth while. All I say is that it's never as much fun to win. Victory is always just a little spoiled by the knowledge that you've had to beat the other fellow and that he wanted to win as badly as you did. But in hockey, or football or baseball—well, I won't say any more. You'll find out."

And Will did find out very quickly. He had never before experienced anything quite like the thrill he got out of a perfectly executed double play, or running the puck through an open field by passing it back and forth to his teammates. It was not long before he had established himself as an athlete of considerable promise, and he reveled in the knowledge that he had gained the respect and admiration not only of his classmates but of the upperclassmen as well.

He learned that even acting in the school plays required teamwork of a different sort. He enjoyed it and received many friendly slaps on the back for comedy parts he played loudly and with great enthusiasm. After two years of such varied but intensive experiences, he even succeeded in evoking loud laughter from his parents when they came to

Andover for the solemn occasion of his graduation and saw
him perform in the senior class play. Actually this was something of an achievement as Mr. Halsted was not much given
to laughter in those trying days.

Whether it was attributable to the nationwide readjust-
ments of the postwar Reconstruction period, or to more
personal reasons, Will learned on his return from Andover
that Halsted, Haines and Co. was having the first setback in
its long, successful history. He also learned—to his great disappointment—that his father had decided he was "too immature" to enter Yale that fall, since he was not yet seven-
teen. After the first shock wore off, Will felt he would like to
show his father that he was wrong. Instead of spending the
summer at Irvington, as he had looked forward to doing, he
volunteered to help out in the office. Mr. Halsted was delighted. But, to Will's surprise, it was Uncle Thaddeus who
was greatly overjoyed. He threw his arms around Will and
hugged him.

"Will!" he exclaimed. "You've proved I was right when I
urged you to go in for sports. You've given a perfect demonstration of team spirit. The family is as much of a team as
any baseball nine. So's the community we live in—and our
country. Remember, Will, what you said about a doctor's
life not being his own?"

Will nodded.

"Perhaps now you'll understand. Being at everyone's beck
and call—always available to serve or to relieve someone's
pain—that is a doctor's life."

"I see," Will agreed. "It's like being part of a team—the
human team."

"A man must lose his life to find it," Thaddeus continued.
"It says that in the Bible. And it doesn't much matter what

he loses it in, so long as he believes in what he's doing. Remember that, boy."

"I will," he promised.

That fall and winter he attended a boys' day school in New York and in the spring began cramming for his Yale entrance examinations.

"You'll make it, all right," his uncle assured him. "You'll get in. What's more, you'll make the Yale football team. I'm planning on coming up to New Haven to root for you in your first game."

But Thaddeus Halsted could not carry out his plan. A recurrence of the swamp fever resulted in a heart attack, and death in midsummer.

It was Will's first experience with death and it affected him deeply, for he had loved Uncle Thad. The fun and excitement seemed to have gone out of everything. When he was notified that he had passed his examinations, he was neither surprised nor elated. Nothing seemed to mean as much as it had before. He would have been content to remain in the office at Halsted, Haines and Co.

He carried this apathy and lack of enthusiasm with him to Yale, with the result that he made few friends and went in for no extracurricular activities during his freshman year. However, another summer at Irvington, working in the greenhouse, riding horseback, and reviving the many happy memories of his boyhood seemed to bring about a change. Possibly his father had been right. Perhaps he had been "immature." He felt now that he had grown up. He made up his mind to face his problems squarely and find a place for himself in the life of the great university.

Chapter
3

ONE NIGHT AFTER A HARD-FOUGHT BASEBALL GAME WITH
Rutgers College which had lasted until darkness stopped
the play, Will was walking home alone. Turning into Chapel
Street on his way to his room in Divinity Hall, he became
conscious of a strange noise. It was not loud, and he wasn't
sure at first that he had not imagined it. He stopped and
listened. There it was again. He turned in the direction
from which it seemed to come, and moved closer. There was
a high wall on his right and a street lamp on his left, and
by the dim gaslight he saw a dark heap up against the wall.
The sound was definitely a whimper, and as Will leaned
closer he made out the form of a small dog. It moved its
head slightly and its two little eyes reflected the light from
the lamp as they gazed pitifully up at him. Instinctively Will
reached down. The dog needed help and he would take it
home and see that something was done. He slipped his
hands under the little body and started to lift the dog. There
was a snarl, and for an instant Will saw a row of white teeth
and felt a sharp pain on his wrist as, quick as lightning, the
dog's head turned back against Will's arm. He drew back in
surprise, and at the same time heard a voice.

"Look out! Leave him alone."

Will looked around. A tall stranger was silhouetted against
the light.

"But he's hurt," Will began.

The stranger interrupted. "But you don't know where he's hurt," he said, squatting down beside the now quiet dog. "You can't just pick him up any old way, like a sack of potatoes."

"Maybe not," Will retorted, "but I just wanted to get him somewhere in the light where I could see."

The stranger didn't answer. He took off his gloves and blew on his hands—long, thin, rather delicate hands. Then he laid one hand on the ground next to the dog's nose, and with the other stroked its head. The thin fingers, white in the lamplight, passed from the dog's head, around his shoulders, along his back, and down his hips. He repeated the strokes several times, pausing every once in a while as though trying to sense something through his fingers. The dog lay quite still, staring at the light and occasionally licking the fingers that were close to his nose. Then the man rose to his feet.

"He has at least one broken rib; and his left hipbone is out of place, though I don't believe it is broken. There is blood near his mouth, so I'm afraid he has some internal injury. It looks to me as if he has been kicked."

"Are you sure?" Will asked dubiously. "How could you tell all that about the ribs—and the hipbone?"

"By feeling," was the reply. "You see, I'm not a dog doctor; but I'm studying anatomy, and there isn't too much difference between the insides of a human and the insides of a dog. I know how the bones ought to feel and—well, that's that. Besides, when you tried to pick him up you bent his body and pushed the hipbone against the sympathetic nerve ganglia that come all the way from the head. Did you ever have a dentist touch a sensitive tooth?"

Will nodded.

"Well, I'll bet you felt like biting the dentist. That's just

how this little fellow felt. Now you wait here. There is a
veterinary friend of mine a block or two off. I'll have him
here in a jiffy."

Left alone, Will stood looking down at the pathetic heap
of brown fur. He couldn't help thinking back to what his
father had said, years before, about man not concerning
himself with the insides of living things, the handiwork of
God. This stranger had found out just what was wrong with
this little dog because he knew what it looked like inside.
Will felt sure that God would approve in spite of his father's
words.

The stranger came back with the veterinary, and together
they slipped a flat sheet of tin under the dog and lifted it
off the ground. The three men with their little burden set
off down the street.

An hour later Will and the tall stranger left the doctor's
house. They had watched the skillful, kindly hands snap
the hipbone in place and splint it, thus easing the dog's
pain. Their role in the matter was over.

"Anatomy must be interesting," Will said. "I'd like to know
more about it."

"Well," replied his new friend, "I can understand that.
You should get the textbook we use here in medical school.
It's pretty tough reading unless you're going to make a
business of it, but I don't know any other way. The book-
store here in town carries it—Gray's *Anatomy*. It's full of
pictures. And then there's Dalton's book on *Physiology*."
The stranger smiled as he added, "But I don't think you'd
better tackle them both."

They reached Will's door in Divinity Hall. "Won't you
come in a minute?" Will asked hospitably.

"No, thanks," replied the other. "I've had a tough week
and I think I owe myself some rest. By the way, my name is

Roger Bacon. You're Will Halsted, aren't you? I saw you play this afternoon. Look me up sometime."

Will had every intention of seeing his newfound friend again; in fact, he wrote his name down on a piece of paper. But so many things occupied his mind that he kept putting it off until even his resolution was forgotten. The baseball season was followed by a summer vacation at Irvington. When his junior year began, he became involved in a project that dwarfed all other interests.

On a Saturday in November he awakened with a start. The game! This was the day of the big game. He kicked free of the blankets and hurried to the window. As he had done every day for the past three weeks, he allowed himself the pleasure of looking proudly at the poster nailed to one of the great elms across the street from Divinity Hall.

CHALLENGE MATCH
YALE vs COLUMBIA
PICKED TWENTIES
TO BATTLE
at
HAMILTON FIELD FAIR GROUNDS
2:00 P.M.
SATURDAY, NOVEMBER 16, 1872

He turned from the dormitory window, grabbed a towel, and hurried down the hall toward the large room with its long row of zinc-lined bathtubs that always looked to Will like a formal naval ceremony of small boats on parade. Other boys in the line saw him and stood aside, voluntarily giving up their turn for a member of Yale's football team. Not only was Will a member of the team but he had suggested to Dave Schaff, the Yale captain, that they might play another college—something Yale had never done. Schaff jumped at the idea and sent out several challenges. Columbia College in New York accepted the challenge. It was to be a tremendous event.

The game was scheduled to be played on the oval at the center of the old Hamilton Fair Grounds race track. One of the old horse barns had been converted into a temporary locker room and dressing room for both teams; but, as there were no showers or running water in the barn, basins, pitchers, and tubs of water had been provided for the visitors, while the Yale team had decided to dress in the dormitories. The Columbia team was due to arrive on the eleven-o'clock train from New York, and the plan was to have them greeted ceremoniously at the railroad station and escorted to the playing field by the whole Yale team.

As Will pushed his way through the crowd on the wooden platform of the New York–New Haven tracks, he was amazed to see that not only a great many undergraduates but apparently all the citizens of New Haven were at the station. Everywhere he went, the jostling, good-natured crowd opened up to make a pathway for him.

"Hi, Will, going to win for us today?"

"That's Will Halsted, one of our best kickers."

"Good luck, Halsted. Show those Columbians what's what!"

"You can do it, boy. Good luck."

Will returned their cheery greetings gaily, and finally succeeded in joining his teammates just as the wailing scream of the train's whistle sounded and the Yale sophomore band sprang to attention and began tuning up.

The first man to emerge from the train appeared to Will Halsted to be bigger than anyone he had ever seen before. He was at least six feet tall and seemed almost as wide. The little blue skullcap perched on the top of his head looked as out of place as an acorn cap on a church spire. Crowding on his heels came a second and a third Columbia player; they both seemed to dwarf the first man. The shouts and laughter of the crowd died away to an awed silence.

"They'll murder us!" Jim Platt exclaimed. "Just tromp us into the ground."

"Cut it out," Dave Schaff said sharply. "They're big all right. But nobody can tell me that anyone that big can be very fast. We'll just have to rely on our speed to get in there and get the ball away from them."

"We'll be lucky if they let us get anywhere near the ball," Babe Olsen muttered. "It's easy enough for you to talk about getting the ball away from them. You're not going to be out there on that field, boy. You can thank your lucky stars you've got a bum leg. *We'll* probably end up in the hospital."

Will pushed his way between them. "Look, Dave," he said earnestly. "I think we'll have to cook up some plans. You can't play anyway. You do the honors and escort the Columbians out to the Fair Grounds. If you'll okay it, I'll go to the baseball diamond with the rest of the team and we'll try to work out a defensive strategy."

"Defensive strategy never got a team anywhere, Will," the captain answered. "It's the team with the best offense that wins. If you can whip up something that will let us get just one goal, it'll at least save us from getting whitewashed."

"We can't be any worse off than we are," Jim Platt admitted.

Will left, signaling for his teammates to follow him.

Fifteen minutes later the boys crowded around Will in front of the bleachers of the baseball diamond.

"It's a question of surprise," Will explained. "I've been trying to think it out. It may not work; but if we all give it a try, I think it will."

He jumped onto the players' bench so that he could see all

of them, and noted with pride their eagerness and their
confidence in him.

"You all know that a good, long downfield kick starts low."

Some thirty attentive heads nodded agreement.

"The ball leaves the kicker's foot about two feet from the
ground and rises slowly. It doesn't reach a height of ten feet
until it has traveled about fifteen yards. A guy who's over
six feet tall can block a kick at a distance of fifteen or sixteen
yards from the kicker. Usually our middle men and side
men can give the kicker that much protection and keep the
opponents from getting that close. But where we're faced
with a tribe of Goliaths—"

"You think we should try to kick high up in the air instead
of trying for length?" Babe Olsen asked.

"No good!" Jim Platt exclaimed. "The ball would travel
only about thirty yards and give the Columbians possession
of it too close to our goal line."

"Right," Will agreed. "I was thinking we might try kicking laterally across the field to another—unguarded—player
who'd be waiting for it. Then he could kick for distance."

A chorus of shouts went up as the simplicity of the idea
struck the boys. Suddenly they were all eager to try out a
brand-new idea that would call for signals and the closest
possible teamwork. For nearly two hours they tried out
Will's idea. Then with dawning hope and great excitement
they headed for the Fair Grounds.

At the corner of Chapel and College streets they found a
large group of students waiting to escort the team to the
field. Banner-bedecked carriages had been hired. The horses
had blue streamers attached to their harnesses. It was quite
a procession, and for the whole length of the two-mile route
to the Fair Grounds it kept gathering participants—gentry
in carriages, men on horseback, men and women on bicycles,

people walking alongside, singing Yale songs and cheering the team. Will had no idea that this game would be considered so big an event, and he couldn't help feeling important as the parade moved on toward its goal. The entrance to the Fair Grounds resembled the gate of a castle, and as his carriage drove across the imitation drawbridge Will felt like a knight entering the jousting arena to do battle in a tournament.

The Columbia team was warming up on the green oval. Surrounding it were people everywhere. Will had expected an audience of a few hundred at most. As he looked around and across the field, he realized that there must be nearly two thousand spectators, and they had paid twenty-five cents each to watch Yale play! It only strengthened his determination to do everything possible to help Yale win. He jumped out of the carriage and ran over to Dave Schaff, standing in the doorway of the locker room. Others were there ahead of him, slapping Dave on the back, telling him his worries were over, and exclaiming about the great possibilities of Will's idea.

"It'll probably work for one play," Dave conceded. "But once they're onto it, I don't see why they should be fooled twice."

He looked around the circle of long faces and grinned. "Anyway, it's certainly worth a try."

He hobbled over to Will. "I just want to say I think it's great the way you figured this thing out," he said. "How do you plan on telling each man who's going to receive the lateral kick?"

"Everyone's got a number, Dave. Jim calls out the receiver's number, and the kicker knows just where to aim the ball. The whole plan depends on accurate kicking rather than powerful booting."

"Well—we're counting on you, Will! We've done the challenging and we want to win this game badly. You're one of the best men we have."

There were those words again—"one of the best." Will liked the sound of them. Somehow to be one of the best put a man in a fine group and gave him the feeling of pulling together with other good men.

The field judge ordered the teams to take up their positions. The Columbia team scattered over their end of the field with no particular formation. The Yale men, on the other hand, took very careful positions. At the goal posts were the two "keepers," and on their right and left two "side men." At a considerable distance from and in front of the goal were the "middle men," eight in number and arranged like a crescent with its horns resting on either side of the field. In the center of the crescent were the six "rushers," who were to follow the ball wherever it went and who, as they were to do the hard fighting, were the heaviest men on the Yale side. The "peanutters," who were to keep ahead of the ball and kick it over when it neared the Columbia goal, completed the arrangement.

Yale lost the draw and Columbia chose to receive. To the Yale rooters this seemed disastrous. They realized that the powerful Columbia team might get a goal in the opening moments of the game.

One of the three field judges blew his whistle. Yale's "peanutters," "side men," and "middle men" surged forward in formation as Jim Platt's foot met the ball and sent it sailing far downfield toward the Columbia goal. The game was on! In the opening moments it looked very much as if Yale's worst fears would be realized. The Columbia men surged up the field like a released avalanche. It seemed as if nothing could possibly stem their uninterrupted advance toward the Yale goal. But, miraculously, something did.

Little Jimmie Forbes, one of the "peanutters," somehow managed to wedge himself into the very center of the melee and get his toe on the ball. He dribbled it out some ten feet. The Columbia giants quickly lined up defensively between him and the goal, but they were completely unprepared for his next move.

"Seven!" he shouted, and, turning, faced his own goal. "Seven" was Jim Platt's number, and he stood ready almost in the shadow of Yale's goal posts. Jimmie kicked directly at him—and a gasp went up from the crowd, who thought that the midget Yale man had panicked and accidentally kicked in the wrong direction. Jim waited for the ball to bounce. Then, calmly and with perfect timing, he booted it far down the field. There, waiting for it, was Will Halsted, alone and completely unguarded. Grinning with a sense of complete satisfaction, he kicked the ball low and accurately to Babe Olsen, who promptly kicked it over the Columbia crossbars. Yale had scored in less than a minute after the opening whistle. For a moment the crowd sat stunned. Then a roar broke out that, to Will, seemed loud enough to be heard back on Chapel Street, two miles away.

Yale's triumph was short-lived. It was an angry and disgruntled Columbia team that lined up to receive Jim Platt's second kickoff. And this time there was no stopping them. They surged up the field, using their superior weight to block off any interference. Moments later, unhampered by any Yale player, they kicked the tying point.

Back and forth, up and down the field, the dark blue and light blue uniforms surged and flowed, but neither team was able to break the tie. A ten-minute rest period was allowed after the first hour of playing time. As the teams trotted off the field, Dave Schaff threw away his cane and hobbled out to meet them.

"You were great! Every single one of you. Simply great!"

he shouted. And then he linked arms with Will and Jim, who half carried him back to the players' bench where the Yale team was to have its huddle while the visitors had dressing-room privileges. "Even though the rules say that the best five out of nine goals are needed to win, in the event of the game's having to be called on account of darkness it's the team that's ahead that wins. So we've just got to get one more point."

"Trouble is," Jim said, "we're tiring more than they are. That's where their greater weight tells. So even if we do manage to get another goal, they'll get the ball on the kickoff and plow through us to tie it all up again."

"Why couldn't we use the new tactics defensively?" Will asked. "Instead of rushing them after the kickoff and simply being bowled over like ninepins, why don't we line up thirty yards from the goal and just concentrate on keeping them from scoring?"

"It's worth a try," Dave agreed. "First we've got to get one more goal."

"That'll be a cinch," Will said confidently, and grinned.

They did get another goal a few minutes after the start of the second half. Will's expert toe connected with the ball and sent it straight across to Jim Platt on the side of the field, and Jim calmly booted a long, straight kick over the Columbia crossbar. From here on, Yale managed to block every effort of the Columbia men to get the tying point. Yale's first intercollegiate football game ended in a glorious victory.

Will had played hard; he had done his best because that was the way he liked to do things, not with any thought of glory. He was genuinely surprised when, shortly after the game, he was unanimously elected captain for the following year. He received congratulatory letters from his old school-mates, and even one from his father, who, however, reduced the glory of the whole thing by ending the letter with "I must remind you that there are more important things than football." This, Will knew, meant Halsted, Haines and Company, dry goods. The least he could do for his father would be to get a degree—something to which he had up to now given very little thought. He made up his mind, though not with any great enthusiasm, to give it thought, and try to prove to his father that he could do something besides play football.

THUMBNAIL

Chapter
4

THUMBING THROUGH THE CARD CATALOGUE IN THE LIBRARY one day, Will saw a familiar title, *General Anatomy* by Henry Gray. He started to turn the card, but hesitated. Why not take the book out? For a long time he had intended to look it over. He filled out a withdrawal slip and returned the card to the file. He moved down the row of wooden file cabinets and pulled out another drawer. On a second withdrawal slip he wrote *"Physiology* by John Dalton," and presented the two slips to the librarian.

With the two heavy books under his arm he crossed College Street and ran up the three flights of stairs to his room in Divinity Hall. His roommate was at class; the street was quiet. He sat down at his desk and opened *General Anatomy* by Henry Gray. He turned to the end. There were eight hundred and fifty pages. He let them fall slowly through his fingers, stopping to glance at the pictures and chapter headings. There were words he had heard though he had never given them much thought: nervous system, veins, arteries. There were other words he had never heard. They looked like a lesson in his Latin grammar. Trying to pronounce them was a little like tasting new varieties of candy—bitter, sweet, hard, pleasant, and unpleasant. He stopped once in a while and read a little of the text to help him understand some word. It became a sort of game.

The illustrations fascinated him even more than the words. Here were pictures not only of the insides of a frog but of the insides of human beings—figures with all the skin cut away. Here was a man's throat and mouth, not just an expanse of skin and two lips but a complicated mass of veins, arteries, and muscles. It was not unlike some of the thickets he had pushed his way through as a boy, with vines crossing and crisscrossing each other.

On another page were the joints of a man's thigh, held together by a sheath of long muscles that reminded him of the strings of a harp or the warp on a weaving frame. Each picture was a glimpse into a new and mysterious world, one that was everywhere, all around him every day, but never seen. Only doctors knew it well, and if things went wrong inside the body, they could find the trouble and fix it, just as Roger Bacon had done a year ago with the helpless little dog.

Will turned to the introduction to the book. It was short. It said that anatomy is a study of the structure of the body before life is put into it. This was much like an architect's view of a beautiful but empty house, Will thought, before it is animated by the joyous vitality of living persons. He closed the book and leaned back in his chair. Suddenly his mind seemed to be clearing. He experienced the same reaction he had once felt as a small boy when, lost in some tangled woods, he had suddenly come upon the right trail.

With his heart beating faster, he opened the other book and read the introduction. Physiology, he learned, is a description of the body in a state of activity. Will smiled at his comparison of the anatomy of the body with the frame of a house, and now here was the activity of the body and the vitality of the people living in the house. He rather liked the image. It seemed to cover everything. He thumbed through the book. There was a picture of a frog, and in half a page he learned more about it than he could have hoped to, years before, when his father had rebuked him. From the tadpole he turned to the growth of a human baby, ugly and helpless at first, like a little dwarf curled up in a hole. There were chapters on diseases, more different kinds than he had ever thought existed. He had seen sickness in his life, and even remembered visiting in a house where a young child had died of diphtheria. He had had his own fair share of children's diseases, and they had all been just a little mysterious. Uncle Thaddeus had always used the expression "every disease in the book," and here they all were—a chapter on each with terrifying pictures of swellings, tumors, and other strange growths.

There were two chapters on the diseases of the digestive system. Anything that went wrong with the digestion had always meant a stomachache and, to Will, was simply that and nothing more. Not so, he found, according to Dalton. The trouble might be anything from the lips to the stomach, with all sorts of odd organs in between to get out of order.

Will was just beginning to read about a thing called the "pancreas" when the door burst open and his roommate shouted at him, "So there you are! Where have you been all day? I saved you in history by answering for you, but you're going to have some tall explaining to do to old Tankurs in the Greek seminar."

"He was mad, was he?" Will asked rather indifferently.

"In a sort of Greek way," his roommate replied, laughing. "He muttered 'adunetos pais,' which—if you have followed the course at all—you should know means 'impossible boy.' "

Will put a bookmark in Dalton's *Physiology*, linked his hands behind his head, leaned back in his chair, and smiled at his friend. "Tankurs is narrow-minded," he said. "I wonder if he was ever young."

"Maybe not, but between him and the dean you'll get pushed out of college before you graduate if you don't watch out. You may be a football hero, but they don't give degrees for that. What's the idea anyway, Will?"

"Oh, I was reading." How could he possibly make anyone really understand his sudden, new enthusiasm.

His roommate looked at the books on the table. "Anatomy!" he exclaimed. "That's all about bones, isn't it? Dry, rattling bones?"

"Only when they're dead," Will shot back, "like Greek."

"How long have you been going in for this sort of thing?"

"Since this morning."

"Never heard of the course. I thought they taught that only in medical school." His friend glanced at the clock, and added, "By the way, I thought you said something yesterday about final practice for the Eton game. It's three o'clock now. Or have you given up football for anatomy?"

Ordinarily Will would have sprung to his feet in dismay at the thought that he, the captain of the team, was late for practice, but suddenly it didn't seem too important. The visions aroused by the medical books had opened to him long vistas into his own future that made football and baseball seem utterly insignificant. Graduation was now not only a matter of satisfying his father and his own pride; it was vital to his entire life, a gateway to a dream that must become a reality.

But here was a game that was immediate—one that concerned others besides himself. He couldn't let any of them down. He smiled faintly as his roommate continued to protest, picked up his coat and left the room.

Eton School in England had sent over a team picked from among its graduates to play Yale. This was a game that Will badly wanted to win. It represented the culmination of his

football playing, and he wanted to justify his teammates'
faith in their captain. Things worked out in story-book
fashion. The game was closely contested every inch of the
way. Will Halsted kicked the tie-breaking goal and was
carried off the field on the shoulders of his teammates.

With the game behind him, Will returned to the two
leather-bound books. They intrigued him and he read more
and more of the details, but he wanted to see the pictures
and descriptions come alive. He wanted to see things firsthand. A day or two later he carried out his delayed promise
and looked up Roger Bacon at the medical school. Certainly,
Bacon assured him, he could attend a surgical clinic. In fact,
he would take him to one himself. Will soon found himself
sitting among twenty or thirty medical students in the operating theater of the Connecticut State Hospital, where, Roger
explained, all the medical-school clinics were held. The Yale
medical students were given a complete cross section of the
work of a surgeon.

Will took in the scene with interest. The wooden benches
rose in tiers, and he had a good look at the room below. The
floor was almost entirely taken up with what looked like
half of an enormous barrel. Inside was the operating table
surrounded by the black-robed surgeon and his assistants.
On a shelf attached to the inside of the barrel-shaped amphitheater were rows of black-handled instruments, shiny and
efficient. Roger explained to Will that the man leaning over
the patient's head was about to administer the ether—the
drug most favored by American surgeons to produce unconsciousness. The body, partly covered by a sheet, lay stretched
out, looking very white and rather pitiful. It reminded Will
in a grotesque way of the dead frog pinned to white wrapping paper years ago in his own home, its little white belly

upturned, ready for the hesitant razor that finally peeled away the skin and brought parental wrath down on the head of the youthful operator.

The surgeon at the operating table showed no hesitation and went to work with confidence and skill. The students around Will whispered to one another, but otherwise the room was quiet. The group at the table worked silently except for an occasional word of command from the surgeon.

When the operation was over, Will walked out with Roger Bacon.

"Well, what do you think of it?" his friend asked.

"It's completely fascinating," Will said.

"Why not study medicine? Or maybe you're going to. I never had a chance to ask you what you are going to do."

Bacon had said aloud what Will was thinking, but he merely replied, "I'm supposed to go into my father's dry-goods business."

Bacon laughed. "Sounds pretty dull to me. Why not talk it over with the old man?"

It was Will's turn to laugh. "You don't know my father," he said. "You don't just talk things over with him. I'll simply have to tell him if I decide to do it."

That night Will lay awake. He wished again that Uncle Thaddeus were alive, with his practical, down-to-earth advice. He tried to think what that advice would be, and the more he thought the more convinced he became that the old doctor would have told him to follow his inclinations. By morning he had made up his mind. He would study to be a doctor. Telling his father would be a bridge he would cross when the time came.

His graduation in June was a rather drab affair for Will. His mother had a cold and couldn't come up to New Haven, and his father didn't wish to leave her. The bright spot of the occasion was his degree. There were, to be sure, no honors attached to it, but Will felt that it was a symbol—the first step to being a doctor.

At home he found his mother resting in bed. She was most sympathetic to his talk of the unimportant memories of the last few months of college. She unrolled his degree, read it carefully, and congratulated him. Will had decided not to tell her of his plans until after the interview with his father, but she was so sympathetic and his future was so much on his mind that he told her of his decision. She lay still on the pillow when he was through, a little puzzled frown taking the place of her smile.

"I'm afraid your father won't like this, Will."

"I guess you're right, Mother."

"There is a special reason, which I'm sure your father will explain to you," she went on. "The firm is in some difficulty financially. I think he is counting on you."

This was, Will thought to himself, an appeal to family loyalty, a complication he hadn't foreseen.

"I would be no good," he said aloud. "I'm not a businessman. Let Dick take over. He has a flare for that sort of thing."

"Dick is only eighteen," his mother protested.

"Young blood—that's what the firm needs," Will argued. He patted his mother's hand. "I'm sorry, Mother, if I make things difficult for you, but I can't change my mind."

Mrs. Halsted knew the stubborn streak in her son; so she made no further attempt to dissuade him, and changed the subject. "Do you remember your old schoolmaster, Mr. Tufts?" she asked.

Will nodded, a little at a loss as to why she should suddenly ask such a question.

"He is coming to dinner tonight. I want to be at the table, so I am resting now. Minnie and Bertha will have their supper early. Dick begged off. He said Mr. Tufts spoils his appetite. I—I hope, Will, we can have a pleasant evening."

Will smiled. "I'll do my best, Mother," he said. "With the Reverend Mr. Tufts present, I doubt if Father will discuss personal family affairs."

Will was right about his father, but not about Mr. Tufts.

"So you are a graduate of Yale," he said, purring with pride as though he himself were responsible. "That's fine— fine. I went to Williams myself; but then, Yale is a good school too. Do you have any plans for the future?" Then, without waiting for an answer, he added, "I suppose you will join your father's firm."

The silence that followed this remark was something like a pause on the stage when an actor has missed a cue. Will glanced at his mother questioningly, but received only a rather frightened smile.

"My son, Mr. Tufts, will follow tradition, and become the third Halsted in the firm founded by my father. His degree from Yale, while honorable, will of course not entitle him to any very prominent position at first, but I fully expect that, with experience, he will qualify to take my place when I—er—cease to be active."

Mr. Tufts's head was nodding slightly all through this speech, the color was rising in Mrs. Halsted's face, and Will's heart was making noises like a muffled drum. There was a tense moment of silence when Mr. Halsted finished. His mother had said that she hoped they could have a pleasant evening, and he had fully intended to do all in his power to make it so, but his father's dictatorial words made him forget all his good intentions.

"I'm sorry, Father," he said, looking straight at the elder Halsted, "but I'm afraid I have other plans."

His father sat back in his chair and looked at his son in amazement. "And what might they be?" he asked in a tone that clearly implied that no other plans were possible.

"I plan to study medicine. In the fall I shall enroll at the College of Physicians and Surgeons here in New York."

In the silence that followed, Mr. Tufts asked brightly, "How do you feel, sir, about having another doctor in the family?"

"I see that to answer your question properly, Mr. Tufts, I must quote this young man's grandfather. More than thirty years ago he wrote me a letter. In it there was a certain passage that I have never forgotten. He said, 'If my children do not do well I shall be unhappy. I trust they will always seek to do right and be preserved from evil ways!' I can only repeat that as an answer."

Mr. Halsted was a wealthy man and Mr. Tufts's school was consistently in need of money. On the other hand, Mr. Tufts was a man of God and, as such, it was his duty to bring peace and concord into the lives of those in any degree at odds with each other. He felt that he must say just enough to help the son without in any way antagonizing the father.

He cleared his throat and spoke with his eyes neutrally fixed on his plate. "How very wise your grandfather was, young man! Christ healed the sick and that made his Father happy. I feel sure that you will make your father happy in your chosen work."

The rest of the dinner passed off not too unpleasantly. When Mr. Tufts had bowed himself out, and Mrs. Halsted had gone back to her room, Mr. Halsted asked Will to come to his study. He sat behind his desk and motioned Will to a chair.

"You really mean what you said at dinner?" he asked.

"I know you want me to do well," Will replied, "and I feel that I could not as a businessman. Yes, sir, that must be my answer."

His father pushed back his chair and, rising, went to the

window. He stood looking out, his hands under his coat tails as was his habit when faced with a problem. He spoke without turning around.

"I should like to ask, since you have made such a firm decision, whether or not you have given the question of money any consideration? They don't put you through medical school for nothing."

Will had thought of this. The small allowance that his father had given him when he went to college would be adequate with economical living. It suddenly occurred to him that his father, feeling as he did about his son's future, might easily refuse to continue the allowance. He dismissed this thought immediately, though. His father had unbreakable convictions, but he was scrupulously fair.

"I can manage, Father," he said confidently.

Mr. Halsted continued gazing out the window. "I hope so," he said sharply. "Your Uncle Thaddeus couldn't, as I found to my cost. I am a man of business, William, and I agreed some years ago to give you a small allowance. That is a contract, and I shall observe it; but you need not expect any additional help. Our present financial difficulties, of which you seem to have heard, would not permit it even if I were inclined to support you in this—er—ridiculous undertaking."

Will looked at his father's back. He detected a movement of the hands under the coat tails, and knew what effort the older man was making to control his feelings. He rose and went to the door. "Thank you, Father. I hope that someday you may be proud of me."

Chapter
5

NOTHING MORE WAS SAID ABOUT WILL'S FUTURE. THE OLDER man's disappointment would not allow him to give his son any encouragement, and it was entirely up to Will to prove whether or not his father would ever be proud of him. The long summer in Irvington drew to its close and the family moved back to their city home at Fifth Avenue and Fourteenth Street. His father's business routine began again; his sisters, Minnie and Bertha, and his younger brother, Richard, had their own interests; and Will was left to himself to wait for the opening of the college in October. He studied the catalogue carefully and found that to get a degree in medicine he must attend two full courses of lectures, study medicine for three years, be twenty-one and of good moral character. This was all fairly simple and the tuition was moderate, one hundred and eighty-five dollars plus the cost of as many of the special courses as one cared to take. There was also a summer session which he could attend for an additional thirty dollars. These fees were within his means.

He haunted the area around the college at twenty-third Street and Fourth Avenue. It was, he found, quite a medical center. On the same street was one of the largest city dispensaries, where poor people were treated free of charge;

three blocks farther uptown was Bellevue Hospital; and only a short distance downtown was the New York Eye and Ear Infirmary with, the catalogue said, an average of ten thousand patients a year. Often he went farther afield and walked to the new Roosevelt Hospital, at Fifty-ninth Street, which had been open for only two years. He steeped himself in everything that had to do with medicine.

At last, October came. He walked over to Fourth Avenue and took the horse car to Twenty-third Street to register. It reminded him a little of the first time he went out for the football team at Yale. He had felt a little lonely then, and he felt even more so now. He stood across the street and gazed for a minute at the college. It was not imposing—a square, almost unadorned three-story building with two pairs of steps on the Twenty-third Street side and a row of shops on Fourth Avenue. It was not at all like any of Yale's ivy-covered buildings, steeped in tradition, but it had a quality of efficient reality that Will liked. It was here that he was going to work out his dream.

With his mind on the future, he stepped off the curb to cross to the college. There was a shout; Will had a fleeting glimpse of a pair of horses and the mudguard of a carriage, and the next instant felt himself dragged to the sidewalk.

"That's no way to cross the street," his rescuer said, laughing.

"Stupid of me," Will replied. "Thanks for pulling me out. I guess I was thinking of something else."

"Never do that in New York," the other man advised him. "They drive like the dickens here. Over there at medical school we always say that we get all the clinical cases we want within two blocks."

Will looked up with interest. "You're a student at the college?" he asked.

"Yes. Second year, starting now."

"That's funny," Will said, smiling. "When you pulled me back I was heading for the college, to register."

"I sort of saved you for medicine, eh? I hope the world will remember that when you're famous. Let's get over there while we have a chance."

When the two reached the entrance, the stranger held out his hand. "My name is Sam Vander Poel. Maybe I can help you get started."

"I'm Will Halsted, and I'd appreciate any advice."

"Are you Halsted of Yale?"

"Well, that's my name and I went to Yale."

Vander Poel stared at Will in open admiration. "Gosh, it's not often that this staid old building has welcomed one of the brawny boys. Usually it's the scrawny, string-bean type like me that's attracted to medicine. If I'm not mistaken—and I'm sure I'm not, in spite of your modesty—you were pretty generally known as one of the best all-round athletes Eli ever turned out."

This was said with such a friendly smile that Will's usual shyness fell from him. He no longer felt frightened or alone. He grinned broadly at his newfound friend.

"Come on then. Since you're the brainy type, show me where I sign up. Of course I'll have to make an X. You know —meat-headed athlete."

Sam laughed, and the two young men ran up the steps together. The doors swung open and in a moment the walls of the College of Physicians and Surgeons closed about them. Vander Poel guided Will through the crowded corridors, visiting one office after another where Will answered questions and filled out papers. He found it necessary to register under some one doctor as his preceptor, and as Uncle Thaddeus had often spoken of a Dr. Henry B. Sands, Will decided on him.

"Sands is a good man," Sam assured him. "He's been here

since 1856. Professor of Anatomy. Are you planning to specialize in that?"

Will had discovered his liking for medicine through Gray's *Anatomy*, and his interest naturally lay there; but when the question was suddenly put to him, he was hesitant.

"There's physiology," his friend explained when he saw Will's hesitation. "John Dalton is the best man in that field. He's working on cerebral localization and problems of digestion. You might register under him. Then, of course, there are men in the surgical division."

Will still hesitated.

"Tell you what," Vander Poel suggested. "After a month or so here, have a talk with Dalton. He'll help you make up your mind if anyone can. He's older than Sands and has had a varied career in medicine, including Civil War service. I'll see that you meet him."

For the moment Will decided to leave it at that. He registered with Sands, but there was still a disturbing number of alternatives, suggested by what the catalogue called "College Cliniques," as well as the list of faculty members and the courses of special instruction. He read them over several times: Clinical Surgery, Pathology, Materia Medica, Analytical Chemistry, Diseases of the Eye and Ear, Diseases of Women and Children, Diseases of the Blood Vessels. All were necessary to the training of a doctor, but the choice of a special field was a real problem. Many a night he lay awake going over the list, and fell asleep to dream of a nightmarish jumble of medical terms.

He found Sam Vander Poel helpful, although only slightly more experienced than he was himself. As the weeks went by, the two young men became close friends and soon Sam was a regular visitor at the Halsted house. Before long, Will realized that he was not the only attraction. His sister Minnie took most of Sam's attention. The talk was seldom about medicine when Will's father was present. Sam was most tactful, and managed to develop a great interest in business and flowers which endeared him to Mr. Halsted.

Through Sam, Will finally met Dr. John Dalton. By that time he had attended his lectures in physiology, and had come to admire him as a professor and lecturer. Dalton was more than twice Will's age, but the acquaintance developed into a genuine friendship. The student's eagerness for knowledge appealed to the older man and he took Will under his wing, urging him to use his study and help him in his laboratory.

One day in Dalton's study, when Will had repeated how difficult it was for him to decide on a specialty, the professor smiled. "Your problem, Halsted, is not a new one, although I admire your unusual concern over it. I've been a doctor for more than thirty years, and it happens that I am interested in the physiology of the body. Remember, though, that I had to make my decision just as you have to make yours. I worried over it in the same way. I tried everything. I even had to do surgery during the late war."

"And you gave it up?" Will asked, a little surprised.

"Yes," Dalton replied after a pause. "I gave it up. I hesitated because I want you to understand just why. I was, as I said, interested in physiology, but that wasn't the only reason. Surgery in the field twelve years ago was a pretty unpleasant business, and that's putting it mildly. We surgeons were lucky if we got one night in three for sleep. Even then we were so nervous and played out that sleep was impossible."

"But the surgery itself," Will asked, "wasn't that interesting?"

"That depends on your idea of interesting. Civil War surgery was, of course, concerned chiefly with wounds.

Those that didn't heal we had to get rid of by amputation. We had to dose the poor fellows with whisky and rum, and even then hold them down by force. Hundreds of major operations were performed without any anesthetic at all."

"Couldn't you use chloroform or ether?" he asked.

Dalton shook his head. "In base hospitals, yes; but you must remember that chloroform and ether were hard to get, especially in the field. It was even worse in the South, where they had to smuggle it in from London by blockade runners or from the North in the petticoats of loyal Southern women. I could tell you many exciting stories of the smuggling not only of chloroform but of quinine and morphia." Dalton's eyes had a faraway look as he continued. "I can see them now, the pitiful wounded men waiting their turn, suffering from heat and flies, breathing air filled with the stench of decay and death. When each man's turn came, what did it mean? Pain, amputation—and generally the loss of life. No— after that, surgery had no charm for me. But of course that doesn't mean it might not have for you."

Will pursued the matter. "Did you have to amputate?"

Dalton shrugged his shoulders as he answered. "There was no other way to prevent the spread of infection. No one understood where it came from or how to check it. It was generally amputation or a man's life. In those days we called it a miasma or exhalation that came from the infected men and entered the blood of the other wounded. There was no way to fight it."

Will persisted. "What about Lister and his carbolic acid spray?"

Dalton gave a surprised laugh. "You'd better check your history, Halsted. Let me bring you up to date. When the Civil War was only three years old, Louis Pasteur was just experimenting on fermented milk. His findings, as I'm sure you know, were that certain very tiny but actually living organisms were the cause of fermentation or putrefaction in milk and wine. Boiling, or even intense heating, seemed to kill them. This fact set Joseph Lister, the English surgeon, to thinking. If these organisms of Pasteur, he reasoned, were the cause of putrefaction in milk or wine, why might they not exist in a putrefying wound, and why might they not be killed as easily?"

"But you can't boil a wound," Will interrupted.

"Exactly," Dalton agreed, "but Lister was not a man to be easily licked. He kept his eyes and ears open. Shortly after Pasteur had announced his discovery, Lister heard of a certain Dr. Crooks who had succeeded in taking the odor out of the sewage in a large industrial town by the use of a chemical which he called 'phenol'. This, as you know, is carbolic acid, a coal-tar preparation. Simple reasoning suggested to Lister that the odor of sewage was due to putrefaction and decay, just as in the case of milk or wounds. The year after the Civil War he performed his first operation with carbolic acid applied to the wound in dressings. The patient was a young boy with a compound fracture, and the treatment was surprisingly successful." He spread his hands in a gesture of finality. "That's a long answer to your question, but I think you can see why we surgeons in the Civil War had to bear with the foul odors, and why we talked of miasmas. After all, Pasteur's germs were born in the air. We were right to that extent. Most American doctors are opposed to Lister, and use his carbolic acid spray carelessly if at all. So, naturally, there is still infection."

In the brief silence that followed Dalton's explanation, Will began a train of thought. He sensed a trail that was worth following.

"It seems to me," he said finally, "that it is quite possible there is some other source. Surely the indifference of even many doctors could not account entirely for the continuing infection."

Dalton smiled patiently. "Why doesn't that answer your problem?" he asked. "Take up surgery as your field and find that other source." Seeing a look of interested agreement in Will's eyes, Dalton continued. "If you should decide that way, the best place in New York for you would be Bellevue Hospital."

"But what about all the criticism I read in the papers last year?" Will put in. "The death rate there—and the bad conditions?"

"That was true," Dalton agreed. "The place was overcrowded and the death rate in maternity cases was fifty per cent. The newspapers were quite right in saying that the hospital was totally unfit to house the sick. I think those were the exact words. But all that has been changed. The number of beds has been reduced to six hundred and all maternity cases have been removed entirely. They've even built special towers for the toilets, to reduce what is commonly called 'hospital miasma,' the cause of much infection, and they spray the rooms and wards with chlorine gas."

"How about the surgical work?" Will asked.

"That's really why I mentioned it. They have four surgical divisions with a very high percentage of accident cases— cuts, serious wounds, amputations. Dr. James R. Wood has the chief surgical clinic—one of the best surgeons we have, although I don't believe he is too enthusiastic about Lister. They also have organized an ambulance service."

"Can I work there?" Will asked eagerly.

"Only graduates may take the intern examination. Undergraduates used to work there; but after all the furor about conditions at the hospital, they tightened up on the requirements. They demand a competitive examination now. The rule has just gone into effect."

"Are there no exceptions?" Will asked.

"None that I know of after this year. Your friend Vander Poel comes up for his examination in June."

Will was persistent. "Suppose I were to take this examination anyway, as an experiment, and suppose I passed it. Could they actually keep me out?"

Dalton laughed. "You're certainly full of ambition. As I said, it's a very recent ruling. I imagine, if you really qualified, they wouldn't refuse to accept you, although that is no promise. You realize, of course, what it would mean. You will have to cram a whole lot of knowledge into a few months—almost the equivalent of a year of medical school. That's a lot of extra work."

Will smiled with eagerness. Here was something definite. The idea of the extra work meant nothing to him. Bellevue became a goal, and the sooner he reached it the better. He took on extra courses. Dalton let him use his study and laboratory for work and experiments. He carried on chemical tests under the guidance of Alonzo Clark, the president of the college. Somewhere in this field lay the answer he was looking for.

Anatomy and dissection became his chief interests. He gave up his summer vacation at Irvington. Instead, he worked in the Center Street Dispensary, learning all about potions, pills, elixirs, and ointments and helping make up prescriptions. As if this were not enough, Will became a familiar figure at all the so-called "private quizzes." These were organized by the faculty members, and covered the subjects contained in the curriculum. They were really cramming sessions and no student was compelled to attend them, but Will never missed one. Unexpectedly Sam Vander Poel failed to pass the Bellevue examination in June, and Will took on the added burden of tutoring his friend so that they could take the examination together in the fall.

The strain was great, even for Will, and he was forced to give it up for a month or two. He went to Block Island, where he relaxed in solitude—devoting regular but much shorter hours to study. By early autumn he was quite himself again, and went back to New York eager to face the Bellevue examination. This appointment, if he could get it, would mean among other things an opportunity to delve into the causes of infection. He knew that he would be up against real opposition. Lister had just toured the United States demonstrating his carbolic acid spray for killing disease germs in the air. He had been very coldly received by most doctors. As Sam had said to Will one day, "A majority of the doctors in this country look upon infection as just something you have to put up with. Germany's sold on Lister, but not England or this country."

This seemed unbelievable to Will, and at Bellevue he would really find out. He had read all of Lister's writings on the subject, especially his famous speech on "The Antiseptic Principle in the Practice of Surgery," and was fully convinced. His only feeling was that Lister had not gone far enough. He felt sure that there was another source of infection besides the germs in the air. He must find out where this was and the sooner the better. Thus the Bellevue appointment became a vital step in the pattern of his life.

When he and Sam went down to the big rambling structure that was Bellevue, and presented themselves for the examination, Will felt confident. Most of the other candidates were nervous and pale from studying and cramming in the hot city during the summer. Will, however, had developed a healthy coat of tan; his mind was clear and his determination great. A word from Dalton just before the examination was cheering.

"Good luck in the test. Anyone who wants to pass as much as you do can't fail. When you get in, try to work with Tom

Sabine or Stephen Smith. These are two good men who believe in Lister. You should get along well with them."

As they walked home after the examination, Sam too was
in good spirits. They discussed the questions and compared
answers.

"I feel I've done all right," Sam said hopefully. "If I do get
in, it will be due to your tutoring. It's a funny thing," he
added, "but when I dragged you away from that carriage
two years ago I never thought I'd end up by being tutored
by you."

Will laughed. "It's the least I could do for a man who
saved my life. I hope I helped you a little."

The answer to this came a week later, and it surprised
them both. When the results were announced, Sam found
he had made second place, while Will had to be content
with fifth. The difference didn't bother him in the slightest.
Sam, as a graduate doctor, deserved the higher position. As
for himself, he would become a doctor next year and, anyway, he was not after personal glory. He was in Bellevue,
and that was all that mattered.

Chapter

6

WILL DIVIDED HIS TIME BETWEEN BELLEVUE AND THE COLLEGE.
He had to have his M.D. degree, so he could not neglect
his classes; but he regretted the days he had to spend away
from the realistic, human dramas at Bellevue. He found that
Dr. Dalton had been quite right when he told him that the
work there was mostly with accident cases. And every case,
whether trivial or serious, interested Will. He was on the
scent of causes of infection, eager to note common character-
istics that might furnish a clue.

His routine duties kept him in constant touch with the
patients. He had to keep a careful record of the pulse and
respiration of each, and make and record all the chemical
and microscopic tests. In this way he was able to follow
the postoperative course of each one who had undergone
surgery. He made careful observations of the healing process
in those who recovered, and noted what might be the cause
of infection in each of those who died. Often he had to
follow the house physician on his daily rounds, or even
assist at operations.

One day he was assigned to assist Dr. James R. Wood,
who was the chief clinical surgeon and an operator of great
skill. A man shot in a street fight was suffering from a bullet
lodged in his side. It was the first chance Will had had to

see an operation at Bellevue at close hand. He had, together with other interns, watched from the surrounding seats, but now he was to be right at the elbow of a top-ranking surgeon while he worked.

With some misgivings Will put on the coat that was handed to him. It was one used an hour before by another assistant and it was not particularly clean. According to instructions he had prepared a number of needles threaded with carefully greased silk sutures; these he stuck in the lapel of his coat, and waited for Dr. Wood. The great man arrived on time; he was as meticulous about promptness as he was about his surgical technique. He was wearing a black silk robe buttoned tightly at the neck and wrists. A bunch of fresh, bright flowers was pinned to his left breast— a carry-over, Will mused, from the plague year in seventeenth-century London when this was supposed to ward off infection. That Dr. Wood still had faith in it was hard for Will to believe, but it was the great man's unalterable habit to wear the flowers.

As they entered the operating room, Dr. Wood paused and looked about at the group of doctors and interns who were to be his audience. It was a theatrical gesture, deliberately and beautifully timed. Then he approached the operating table and its helpless burden. There was another pause while he checked the anesthetist and the assisting nurses. His eye scanned the instrument table which Will had carefully prepared. The shining scalpels, knives, and forceps, each fitted to carved ivory handles, seemed to meet with his approval, and he turned to the anesthetist and motioned him to start giving the ether. First a wad of cotton was placed over the nose and mouth of the patient, then a cone made of a towel stiffened with a folded newspaper was set over it and through this the pain-deadening ether was poured drop by drop. When he was satisfied that the patient was unconscious, Dr. Wood called to Will for the first instrument.

The surgeon worked fast, with unmistakable skill. If an instrument displeased him he flung it to the floor; paused long enough to berate the instrument maker, who invariably sat in the gallery, and demanded another. After opening the skin, the doctor's agile fingers probed for the bullet. Will recognized the skill and the dramatic speed with which the surgeon worked; but when his fingers became red and sticky with blood and pus, and he wiped them on his robe, Will had visions of the Civil War surgeons and became conscious, again, of the specter of dirt. The handles of the instruments and Will's own hands became sticky. When he pulled the needles from his lapel to hand to Dr. Wood, he wiped his fingers on his coat; but some of the stickiness clung to them, to be wiped off only as the needle was passed through the patient's flesh. Will felt that the whole thing was wrong; that even if the surgeon refused to use Lister's spray, he should at least improve on the Civil War crudeness of procedure. As a very minor assistant who had never performed an operation Will's voice would be unheard, and a feeling of helplessness came over him. Later, when he learned that the patient had developed a high fever, that the wound had suppurated violently, and that the man had died of pyemia, he was not surprised.

He determined to take whatever steps were necessary to enable him to operate, so that he could at least talk or write about his beliefs. Sam Vander Poel was most skeptical about Will's being allowed to operate while he was only an undergraduate intern. But Will reminded Sam that, actually, he had been ineligible when he took the examination for Bellevue. Why couldn't he break another rule? Sam introduced him to Dr. Thomas G. Sabine, a surgeon in another division and a keen follower of Lister's methods. Sabine was struck by Will's eagerness and sincerity. He had a great friend, a Dr. Hamilton, in Will's division, and promised to see what he could do. The doctors' friendship proved most fruitful, for Dr. Hamilton was influential in having many minor surgical cases turned over to Will.

Now was the time to experiment. The surgeon in charge of an operation, even though only an intern, was the final authority. Will began insisting upon hand-washing, clean sheets, and boiled instruments. His methods soon became anathema to the nurses and assistants, who were not used to such procedure, and he was well aware of the rather disgruntled way in which his orders were being carried out. He even devised a hot-bath treatment for patients in whom there was the slightest sign of infection, feeling that the heat which was so effective in Pasteur's sterilization of milk and wine might easily have a beneficial effect when applied to humans.

He kept in close touch with Sabine, and constantly compared results with those of the other surgeons. Their record was good, far better than the others, but still not perfect. The mysterious infections seemed to follow operations with a fatalistic persistence.

In the spring of 1877 he faced the examination for graduation from the College of Physicians and Surgeons. This was for Will a great deal more than a routine test. In the first place he knew that only as a graduate doctor would he be able to continue his search for the lifesaving answer to infection. As an intern he was proving things to himself and to the few others who agreed with him, but only as the holder of the M.D. degree could he ever hope to prove anything to the medical profession.

"Tell you what, Will," Sam said at dinner the night before the examination. "When you pass—as I know you will—join me in Europe. I'm going over in April, and we can meet in

Paris. If the answer to this business of infection is to be found anywhere it will be in some place like Vienna, Munich, or Würzburg."

Will was skeptical. "It will take a lot of proof to convince men like Mason and Mott and a host of other surgeons."

"Perhaps it will," Sam admitted, "but if you are backed up by such men as Von Volkmann and Billroth in Europe, you can tell your American friends to go jump in the lake. I mean it, Will. Those fellows in Germany are so far ahead of us it isn't funny."

The extra work he had put in for the Bellevue examination, his fight against infection, and the support and encouragement of Sam and Dr. Sabine bolstered Will's courage. The next day he not only passed the examination but was fourth on the list. Hardly had he recovered from this surprise when he was told that the ten honor men were to compete in another written examination for what was known as the Examination Prize, which carried with it an award of one hundred dollars. Will found the conditions of this examination rather trying as it was public and was held in the college operating amphitheater with all the seats filled with student spectators. But when he read the questions his spirits rose. The first was on one of his favorite subjects— the arteries of the neck. He forgot all about the gaping students around him and wrote steadily for three hours, then turned in his paper with a confidence which was justified a month later at the college commencement exercises when he found that he had won the prize.

He had graduated with honors; he had won a special prize; but he knew this was only the beginning. He wanted to prove to his father and to his old teachers and classmates at Yale that he could be a success in something besides athletics. He felt that he must find out why wounds still became infected in spite of Lister's methods, and he must learn to do everything possible to reduce the postoperative pain.

Sam's invitation to join him abroad was constantly in his mind, but Will felt very strongly that he needed a little time as a graduate doctor before facing any of the great European doctors. Even his work as an intern at Bellevue, he felt, was not sufficient preparation, although he now had his degree and was accorded more respect by the nurses and orderlies.

Then the opportunity came. The position of House Physician at the New York Hospital was open for competitive examination. Will was getting quite used to taking tests, and the prospect of another one did not discourage him. Besides, it was a definite position with considerable prestige attached to it. The hospital had just been established in its new quarters on Fifteenth Street, and the medical wards had not yet been opened. The surgical wards had been in use under Dr. Charles Knight for only six months, so the work was entirely surgical, which appealed to Will.

Just about the time he took the test, Sam Vander Poel sailed for Europe—repeating his invitation to Will—and a few weeks later Will wrote him an enthusiastic letter:

DEAR SAM:

Shortly after you sailed I took and passed the examination for House Physician at New York. I know you have always said that I took on too much and that I might have a breakdown; but I feel very fit, and the work is too interesting to give up.

It is all surgical, and you know how that appeals to me. Our old friend Draper, who is one of the visiting doctors, urged me to do it. I see a lot of him. He has most amusing evenings, music and talk. I can't wait to join you as we planned. I still don't think Lister has gone far enough. There must be some way to keep the germs from spreading. If they are alive, as they certainly must be, they have to come from somewhere, and I intend to find out where.

Minnie sends you her best. I suspect she would like to use some other, stronger word, but you'd know best about that. She and Mother and Dad may come over while we are in Europe.

Sincerely,
WILL

He spent six months as House Physician, working with such doctors as Charles I. Hackley and Woolsey Johnson, who with Dr. Draper were the visiting physicians. He improved on the charts he had had to keep as an intern, devising a new and simpler system of condensing the figures for temperature, pulse, and respiration, and tracing the curves in different colors. Much of the work was routine; much of it was a challenge; but whichever it was, Will achieved a reputation for doing it well. It was almost as though he were an athlete training conscientiously for a game. He was preparing himself for his coming adventure in Europe, and counting the days.

Shortly before Will was to leave, Dr. William Welch joined the staff. He was slightly older than Will, a graduate from the College of Physicians and Surgeons with the class of 1875, and had just returned from Europe. When Will learned this, he made a special point of meeting him. Welch was a pathologist, not a surgeon. He was interested chiefly in the changes that take place in the body under the influence of disease. To Will this was all a part of the same life problem, and he spent some time in Welch's laboratory talking with him.

"You and I have much in common," Welch said one day. "We both have to fight for what we believe. I happen to believe in finding out by experiment exactly what changes occur in the cells of the body through disease, and saving life by that knowledge. You believe in saving life by finding the cause of surgical infection. Yet look what we are up against." He made a sweeping gesture with his arm. "Look at this tiny laboratory. Hardly room to turn around. Very little more money would give me a proper place to work, but the trustees won't hear of it. I haven't followed the theory of asepsis as carefully as you have, but I'll make a bet with you. If we keep our enthusiasm for what we believe, you will have Janeway and all the others at your feet, and I'll have a proper laboratory and regular classes in pathology. It's up to us. I went to Europe and worked under Virchow, the greatest pathologist in the world. Now you go. See Von Volkmann, Billroth—all the men you can. Then come back and teach what you find."

The next day Will sent a cable to Sam:

ARRIVE PARIS OCTOBER 9, WILL

Chapter

7

THE BOAT TRAIN CHUGGED ITS WAY TOWARD PARIS. WILL HAL-
sted sat in the corner of his compartment feeling thoroughly
relaxed. He watched as the train passed through villages
with neat, square stone houses and winding cobbled streets,
so different from the New England villages to which he was
accustomed. At each crossing the engineer gave a little
toot on his whistle—a distinctly foreign toot. Will had become so used to the routine of hospital life in New York that
every slightly different foreign sound or sight was a new
adventure.

He listened to the French conversation around him. He
even exchanged a few words with the man sitting next to
him—about the weather and the obvious fact that he was an
American on his first trip to Europe. Though quite unimportant, they amused him and made him rather proud of his
French.

At the Gare du Nord in Paris, Will stepped out of his
compartment onto the crowded platform. The news vendors
were crying their wares, and the blue-smocked porters were
arguing shrilly with each other or with some bewildered
tourist. There was a general atmosphere of excitement that
only Frenchmen can put into the most ordinary moments
of life. At the platform gate Sam greeted him with a hearty
slap on the back, and soon the two young doctors were

seated in a *fiacre* and driving through the busy streets to their hotel.

Paris was gay, filled with tourists, after the dark days of the war with Prussia. To be sure, a peace treaty had been signed at Frankfurt; but the war had cost France over a billion dollars, the death of 139,000 of her men and the loss of her most cherished provinces, Alsace and Lorraine. She had suffered the famine and horrors of the German siege, and the cruel suppression of the Commune under Thiers. Will was surprised that, after all this, the people seemed gay. They had even organized an International Exposition in the Champs de Mars. He read in his guidebook that the Exposition was a place "where the enmity of nations has finally given way to friendly emulation," and he prayed that this might remain so.

Sam was full of the spirit of the city and, in spite of Will's eagerness to begin the study and research for which they had come to Europe, he couldn't bear to discuss anything as serious as medicine until they had had a few carefree days. Will enjoyed it all but was not sorry when, after three days, he and Sam took the train for Vienna.

Riding through France, across Germany, and into Austria was almost like passing over sacred ground. It was here that the great men of European medicine and surgery lived and worked. Among them were Richard von Volkmann, Robert Koch, Theodor Billroth, Anton Wölfler, and Ignaz Semmelweis. To the ordinary tourist these were just names; to Will and Sam they represented knowledge and skill that America had not yet fully acquired.

Von Volkmann was a man whom Will particularly wanted to meet since he was the first to adopt the methods of Lister; Robert Koch had succeeded in isolating the germ of at least one disease, an infection in cattle that could be transmitted to humans; Billroth was famous throughout Europe for his skill and resourcefulness in the operative treatment of disease, and the first to remove a tumor from the stomach; Wölfler was Billroth's assistant. Semmelweis, an obstetrician in the Vienna General Hospital, who had discovered the cause of fever in cases of childbirth, had died recently. The whole region was the high altar of their profession, and the two American doctors gazed with reverence at the passing countryside.

Will had become so absorbed in his thoughts that he had paid little attention to the other passenger in the compartment. It was only when he turned his head to answer some question of Sam's that he noticed a heavy-set, very tall man with a thick red beard who was absorbed in a German newspaper. When the conductor asked for tickets he put down the paper and glanced about him. The stranger had friendly blue eyes, and Will was delighted when he addressed them in fair English with a heavy German accent.

"You gentlemen are English?" When he learned that they were American, he seemed slightly disappointed but continued politely, "I have never been in your country, but I have just returned from England and—you do look English. You must excuse the error."

Will hastened to put him at his ease. "This is our first time in Europe. This is Dr. Vander Poel. I am Dr. Halsted."

There was a twinkle in the stranger's eyes as he replied, "What a coincidence! I too am a doctor. Let me introduce myself. The name is Volkmann—Von Volkmann, to be exact." Will couldn't believe his ears. He had hoped to see the great man sometime during his visit to Europe, and here by the merest chance they were face to face. For a moment Will was speechless and, before he could comment on the coincidence, the older man asked a question. "You are here for pleasure—or business?"

Will explained that they were both recent graduates of

the College of Physicians and Surgeons, and that they were
in Europe to observe at first hand the methods of European
doctors and surgeons. "And you, Herr Volkmann," he added,
"are one of the greatest reasons for our coming."

Von Volkmann smiled. "I am very flattered. If I can be of
any service, please do not hesitate."

This was a real invitation to Will to speak up. "Am I right
in believing that you agree with Lister about antiseptic
surgery?" he asked eagerly.

Dr. Von Volkmann seemed pleased that the conversation
had turned to medicine, and his reply was enthusiastic.

"But of course! As a matter of fact, the purpose of my
trip to England was to visit him. I have known him for
some time. He is lecturing now at the Royal College of Surgeons in London, and having a pretty hard time." Von Volkmann shook his head sadly. "The English doctors are as bad
as yours in America."

"You mean they have no faith in his theories?" Will asked.

"Not only no faith themselves; they even discourage the
students who might attend Lister's classes, which are pitifully small. In spite of this he continues to teach—a most
remarkable man."

"What did he have to say about his treatment of wounds,
the carbolic spray and all that?" Will asked.

"It was strange," Von Volkmann replied, "but he was
reluctant to talk about it. He asked me questions instead.
He was at that time still experimenting, and I suppose he
hesitated to make any statement that might prove untrue.
He did something, though, that was better than words. He
was, as you undoubtedly know, professor of surgery at the
Glasgow University. He took me to the Glasgow Hospital
and showed me four patients, all of whom had suffered from
major accidents. All had compound fractures with very
severe lacerations and, in one case, a protruding bone partly

cut away. The pulse in all cases was around one hundred and sixty-eight and could barely be detected." Von Volkmann hesitated. Then he asked abruptly, "What would you gentlemen consider a good prognosis?"

Will looked at Sam, who seemed hesitant; so he answered. "As such things happen in America just now," he said thoughtfully, "and assuming that in all cases the destruction of tissue was most severe, I would say gangrene, erysipelas, or pyemia, and immediate amputation. But, of course, one would have to see the wounds."

"Of course," Von Volkmann replied, "but I assure you they were the worst possible."

"Then I think nine doctors out of ten would give that prognosis or—even death."

Von Volkmann shook his head. "Either your American doctors are blind, Dr. Halsted, and haven't outgrown your Civil War days, or else I saw a miracle." He sat forward in his seat. "In all four cases there was no necrosis, no pus, no smell. Healthy granulation had formed and the skin was knitting perfectly."

The rhythmic whir of the train wheels and a murmur of voices from the corridor were the only sounds for a moment. Then Will spoke.

"It was not a miracle, Dr. von Volkmann. Our doctors are blind to many things. Some of them seem to prefer living in the Dark Ages. But there are a few who go along with Lister. I happen to be one of them. Our Civil War did teach some of us a lesson and, thanks to Lister, the horrors of those days are disappearing. Only—" Will hesitated.

"Go on," Von Volkmann urged quietly.

"I know it sounds impertinent, but I feel that Lister hasn't gone far enough. Even among the operations performed by those who use carbolic acid, both on dressings and as a spray, there is still infection. There must be some

other cause and I want to find out what it is. Lister kills the
infection that is in the air and on the surface of the wounds
with his carbolic acid, but infection still persists. Where *does*
it come from?"

Von Volkmann thought for a moment about what Will
had said. "About thirty years ago a man named Ignaz Semmelweis was faced with an almost identical challenge," he
said slowly. "He had your enthusiasm. His problem was the
spread of puerperal fever in childbirth. He felt he had found
his answer; but no one believed him, and his theories were
scornfully rejected. He fought a losing battle for what he
was convinced was the truth, and finally died—insane. I
have no thought of frightening you. I only mention it to
show the opposition you will have to face, particularly in
America. You must first believe in an idea, and then never
give it up.

"Have you heard of Dr. Robert Koch?"

Will nodded emphatically.

"You know, then," the doctor went on, "that he is a
country doctor in the little-known town of Wollstein. He
has recently isolated the germ of a splenic fever called
anthrax that has been killing sheep all over Europe. Now
the disease can be controlled."

Will nodded again.

Von Volkmann touched his arm confidentially. "What perhaps you do not know is that he is right now conducting
experiments to find out where this germ comes from—where
it actually breeds. Furthermore, he told me that he hopes
to make a similar study of the tuberculosis bacillus. If he is
successful in either of these experiments, you should have
at least a partial answer to your question."

Will hesitated a moment, but it was an opportunity not
to be missed. "I should like to meet him while I am here."

"That should be quite possible," Von Volkmann replied.

"He's an old friend of mine. It can't be right away, though. Perhaps in a month? I should be delighted to have you visit me. My place is not too far from Wollstein."

The three doctors continued to talk as the train sped toward Vienna. At Linz, Dr. Von Volkmann got out with a hearty *"Aufwiedersehen."* Will watched him as he disappeared in the crowd on the platform. He was a real link with the outer world of medicine that Will had only dreamed of before this meeting. He sat back contentedly as the train pulled out of the Linz station for Vienna.

Chapter
8

IT WAS A FULL YEAR BEFORE WILL COULD TAKE ADVANTAGE OF Von Volkmann's invitation. Extraordinary things had been happening in European medicine. Theodor Billroth had removed a tumor from a woman's stomach and, to the amazement of all Europe, she had recovered; Anton Wölfler, his assistant, had devised a method of by-passing the stomach in intestinal operations. European surgeons seemed indefatigable. Sam and Will attended clinics, visited and consulted the doctors, and even assisted at operations.

Sam's interests lay in a different field from Will's, but they compared notes daily. One evening they were relaxing over coffee and cigarettes.

"How are you doing in that brain-dissection session with Meiner?" Sam asked.

"I gave it up," Will answered, laughing. "The old fellow insisted on giving me lectures from his bed before he got up in the morning, and the place was always such a mess that I couldn't concentrate. I'm spending time now with Zuckerkandl."

"His course is as tough as his name, I hear," Sam put in.

"Maybe so, but his skin isn't tougher than anyone else's."

"What do you mean by that?"

"I ought to know. I operated on him today."

"You did what?" exclaimed Sam.

"Yes. He had a small cystic tumor on his right thigh. It pained him a good deal and he asked me to operate."

Sam was nonplussed. "With all these famous surgeons around, he asked *you* to operate?"

"Yes. He said he had watched me at the Billroth clinic, and liked the way I did things. He said he wanted to see at close hand how an American surgeon worked."

"Very flattering."

"Better than that, Sam. He was so pleased that he is letting me use his private laboratory. No one else is admitted, and he has a wonderful supply of material for dissection—tissues—everything."

One day Will received a telegram from his father. He and Mrs. Halsted and Minnie were coming to Europe for a visit, and they wanted Will to meet them in Liverpool. Will knew he should be glad to see his family, but somehow just at this time he resented any interruption. He showed the telegram to Sam, who, to his surprise, seemed delighted.

"But, Sam," Will protested, "their visit will take up so much time here, and don't forget that as soon as possible we must go and visit Dr. Koch."

"You can go without me, and tell me all about it," Sam said casually.

"I don't understand you, Sam," Will said, shaking his head.

Sam laughed. "It's really very simple," he said. "You know, I guess, that I'm very fond of your sister Minnie."

It was Will's turn to laugh. "That's been obvious for a long time."

"Well," Sam continued, "at dinner the night before I sailed, she told me that if she decided to marry me she would come over to Europe." He pointed to the telegram. "She's on her way—so I guess we're engaged. Simple, isn't it?"

Will had to admit that it was and he understood perfectly. It was arranged that he would spend a week with his family, and that Sam would stay on and return to America with them. After all, Sam pointed out, he had already had several months more of Europe than Will.

The visit with his family was pleasant enough—a sort of hasty European tour—but Will was not too sorry when he had to say good-by. He sent a telegram to Dr. von Volkmann, and headed for Halle. He wanted to see him and hold him to his promise to arrange a meeting with Dr. Koch.

At Halle he was warmly greeted with real Old World hospitality. Frau von Volkmann was charming and spoke English fluently, so Will did not have to use his newly learned German.

"Well, my friend of the train," Von Volkmann said, "at last I can offer you the hospitality of my house. You are most welcome, as I'm sure you know. I have a feeling, though, that there is something else on your mind—a certain Dr. Koch, eh?"

Will smiled, a little embarrassed. Von Volkmann put him at his ease immediately. "As a matter of fact, I have written to Koch and told him to expect a visitor in the next two days. So you'll have to hurry. We can enjoy a visit together on your return."

The next day Will left for the little village of Wollstein—not too far from Leipzig, where he was planning later to study skin grafting under Dr. Thiersch. He wasn't too sure just what he wanted to ask Dr. Koch; but he felt they were both on the trail of much the same thing, and thus would easily find a common ground.

Robert Koch was not hard to find. He was as well known

as the old bell tower at the entrance to the village. Will realized at once the differences of opinion about him. Some persons from whom he asked directions were eager to help; others were indifferent or even antagonistic. Soon he found himself at the door of a gabled house on a narrow cobbled street. He hesitated before the low doorway. It didn't seem possible that anything of scientific value could be associated with such a place. Yet this was the house. There was no doubt about it. Will knocked. There was no answer. He knocked again. He heard a chair scrape and shuffling footsteps. The footsteps stopped at the door, and a curt voice asked, "*Wer ist da?*"

"I am a friend of Dr. von Volkmann. My name is Halsted."

The bolt was drawn and the door opened. The curt German question was resolved to a friendly greeting.

"Ah, the friend of Richard. Come in, come in. I am Dr. Koch. I was in my laboratory, and my wife is out. I am sorry to have kept you waiting."

Will took the proffered hand, and felt himself almost pulled into the room. The hand was strong and had the rough, dry feel of skin that has been much exposed to acid. Koch cleared a chair of a mass of papers so that Will could sit down, took the letter from Von Volkmann which Will handed him, pushed his spectacles to the top of his head, and read the brief note. Dr. von Volkmann had spoken of Koch as "the little wizard of Wollstein" because of the magic of his discoveries. It occurred to Will that he might well have called him that because of his appearance. Small and stooped, with an unkempt beard and a thin bald head, Dr. Koch might have just stepped from some medieval legend of witchcraft. When he pushed his spectacles up on his head, Will saw two black-rimmed, bloodshot eyes.

Koch handed the letter back to Will without comment. "What can I do for you, Dr. Halsted?"

Put as bluntly as this, the question seemed unanswerable. Frankly he didn't know. He only hoped.

"I have been operating in New York, Dr. Koch, using all of Lister's techniques. I find infection persists. There must be some sources that are immune to spray and carbolic acid."

"I didn't think American doctors believed in Lister," Koch said suspiciously.

"Many—far too many—don't, but I happen to be one who does. It puts one in a difficult position to believe in something that most people scorn. I want to find these other sources of infection and convince the unbelieving."

Koch nodded sympathetically. "And you want me to help you, Dr. Halsted. My findings are at your service, but no dream is easily realized. It requires great faith, and even then one can be disappointed. When I was very young I dreamed of visiting faraway places. I wanted to see the whole world. But that costs money, which was something I did not have. Do you know what I did instead? I bought a cheap microscope, and I found a world larger than the one in which I might have traveled—a world filled with strange, complicated creatures. They have become my constant companions in my search for the realization of another dream." He broke off suddenly. "But enough of this talk. You would like to see for yourself. Come into my laboratory."

He indicated a rag curtain in the center of a crude, wooden partition that divided the room. The gesture, combined with his natural stoop, had the air of a courtly bow, and Will instinctively returned it as he passed through into Dr. Koch's laboratory.

Any words of praise or congratulation that Will might have wished to say died on his lips. The room contained everything necessary to a laboratory, but it was all in such incredible disorder that it was hard to see how any use could be made of it. There were two or three tables laden with bottles, bowls, and vessels of all sorts, some broken, some empty, and some filled with strange colored liquids. There were kerosene lamps and stumps of candles. Hanging from the ceiling were glass containers and cages filled with white mice and guinea pigs. The center of activity seemed to be a revolving stool in front of a microscope. Over it all hung a heavy, acrid smell—animal, human, and chemical—that at first stifled Will so that he hardly realized that Dr. Koch had continued talking.

"It all began when I was made district physician," he was saying. "In the course of my duties I had to examine sheep that had died of an unknown disease, apparently contracted in the pastures. Since the sheep's spleen turned black, it was commonly called splenic fever—anthrax, the scientists called it. With my microscope I examined the blood and found strange, tiny rods. Let me show you."

Koch sat down in the revolving chair, took a slide from a wooden box, and put it into the microscope. Then he motioned to his guest. Will sat down and, leaning over, adjusted the lens. He felt as though he were on the verge of some discovery as he looked into Koch's new world and saw the strange, rodlike forms. They were not alone but were surrounded by others which at times blotted them out. He looked at Koch for further information.

"That is what I first saw," Dr. Koch went on. "This blood was from a diseased sheep; and when it was injected into a healthy one, the latter also died. Whether the little rods were responsible or not, I couldn't tell. If I could only isolate them, find out where and how they bred! That was my problem, and it became my dream."

"And you solved it?" Will asked.

"Not at first," Koch answered. "I thought I had when I put a tiny drop of blood in the fluid from an ox's eye. I reasoned that it would be free of germs from the outside air and, the fluid being transparent, I would be able to examine the blood without removing it from the fluid. I watched hourly day and night, but in some way other germs got in and again blotted out the rods. It seemed hopeless. Then I hit on an idea."

Koch reached to a rack that was standing near a lighted kerosene lamp, and placed a new slide under the microscope. Silently he pointed to it, and Will leaned over again. This time he saw the rods, but they were the only things visible and they seemed to be constantly increasing. Again he looked to Koch for an answer. This time Koch took the slide from the microscope and handed it to Will. In reality it was two slides; the one on top was normal and the underneath one had a shallow bowl.

"The drop of blood in the fluid is hanging from the upper slide by surface tension," Koch explained. "It has no contact with the outer world. To keep out the air I rubbed oil around the edges. I use Provençal oil because it is less rancid than the common stuff. I kept this at body temperature by means of my kerosene lamp. I then injected this drop of blood into the tail of a healthy mouse, using a stick purified by charring. The next day the mouse was dead. I opened its spleen and found it completely alive with these tiny rods."

The bloodshot eyes looked at Will triumphantly. There was no sound in the laboratory except the restless movement of the little mice in their cages. Then Koch continued. "One experiment was no proof. I repeated it dozens of times. In every case the results were the same."

Will was impressed, but still a little puzzled. "These are germs," he said, "and they obviously cause anthrax, but that still doesn't answer the question—where do they come from?"

"If you had asked that question three days ago, I couldn't have answered it."

"And now you can?" Will asked eagerly.

"In a way, yes," Koch replied cautiously. "I left this slide away from the heat one day. When I looked at it through the microscope, the rods were dead."

"How did you know that?"

"Living germs reproduce continuously," Koch pointed out. "These reproduced not at all. What does that suggest to you, as a doctor?"

"That they needed heat to live."

"Exactly—heat, or the warm body of a sheep."

"But—" Will started to interrupt.

"I know—that didn't answer your question. Even with this knowledge I hadn't found their source. Then I made another remarkable discovery. Not only did these rods die when they were deprived of body heat, but they did something else." He leaned forward until the white of his bald head was very close to Will's face, and his bloodshot eyes seemed to glow. "They lost their normal appearance and turned into spores that continued to live in any kind of temperature. As soon as the temperature rose to that of a normal, healthy animal, they changed back into the rods—or bacilli, as I prefer to call them."

Will thought a moment. "Then you mean that when these germs in the shape of spores are exposed to body temperatures they become disease-bearing bacilli?"

Koch nodded.

"And you say that they can live under any conditions— cold, or dirt of any kind—anywhere?"

Koch nodded again, and a smile of mutual understanding lighted up both their faces.

Chapter
9

BERLIN, HAMBURG, KIEL, LEIPZIG, MUNICH, FRANKFURT. WILL visited them all, studying, operating, lecturing, and talking with the leading medical men. The understanding smile that was Dr. Koch's farewell never left his memory. He knew that, through the efforts of Lister and Koch, surgery had a freedom and scope it had never known before. The only limits to operating, now, were the skill of the surgeon and the cleanliness of everything used in the operation. He frequently glanced at his own hands. He was secretly proud of them, and confident that his fingers could perform the most delicate cutting and suturing. Now, with absolute cleanliness added, his chances for saving human lives were immeasurably increased.

He longed to get back to America and face all those who had scoffed at Lister, but first he paid a farewell visit to Von Volkmann. The great surgeon was delighted to see him, and his eyes twinkled appreciatively as Will described his visit to Koch.

"I let you go alone," his host confided when Will was through, "because I knew you two would be sympathetic, and a third person might have spoiled the visit. Now that you have seen the vast world of terror that lies under Koch's microscope, you have a new obligation. Go home and persuade your American doctors to go along with Lister."

Will smiled rather grimly. "With Lister and Halsted," he said.

Von Volkmann nodded. "It won't be easy. Habits of a century are hard to break down, but I'm counting on you."

Will returned to New York by way of London, where he was shocked to find that, as Dalton had said, the English surgeons refused to acknowledge the effectiveness of Lister's methods and Koch's theories. Well, he thought, let England stay in ignorance until she learns the truth from America.

Shortly after he reached New York, his sister Minnie and Sam Vander Poel were married. The excitement of the wedding, the reunion with his family, and the job of moving into his own house on Twenty-fifth Street left Will little opportunity to see any of his doctor friends, though he was bursting with eagerness to talk to sympathetic listeners.

Finally he found himself at his old college in the office of Henry B. Sands, professor of surgery. Will chose to go to him first, not only because of his position, but also because Dr. Sands had been his preceptor when he entered medical school in 1874. Sands was an ardent follower of Lister's antiseptic methods, and Will felt confident that he would get the sympathy and understanding he so longed for. A great deal had happened in the six years since his first visit to Sands' office. Will looked around him at the familiar pictures on the walls, the books and furniture. Nothing seemed changed except himself. The opening of the door and the cheerful voice of Dr. Sands broke in on his thoughts.

Sands listened attentively as Will told him of his trip. The visit to Dr. Koch interested him especially, and he interrupted many times with questions. When Will finished, Sands got up and went to the window, where he stood silently looking out—for what seemed an eternity to Will. He knew that Sands approved of Lister's methods, and he knew that he was open-minded and friendly. What he wasn't sure of was Sands's reaction to the new theory that he had brought back.

Sands turned back abruptly, as though he had made a sudden decision, and sat perched on the edge of the desk.

"It's tremendous, Will. I had a hunch you would come back with something very special." He paused. "I'm afraid you don't realize just what you are up against. The idea that disease-carrying germs can best be fought by absolute cleanliness is revolutionary. Most of the older men will be blindly prejudiced, and the younger ones will demand to be shown. You'll be fighting an almost solitary battle." He got off the desk and stood in front of Will. "Now I have a confession to make. I've been, in a sense, spying on you. I've been writing to Von Volkmann, and I've had several letters from him. We discussed you at great length, and your visit to Koch."

"Volkmann's a genius," Will put in.

"He thinks a lot of you, too," Dr. Sands went on. "In fact, that's why I began making plans. It was his last letter, written after you had seen Koch, that set me thinking."

Will looked inquiringly at his old teacher as Sands continued, "As you may or may not know, one of my positions is that of Attending Surgeon at the new Roosevelt Hospital on Fifty-ninth Street. Erskine Mason, with whom you worked at New York Hospital before you went abroad, is on the Medical Board, and Dr. Draper is the Attending Physician. You know these men and, while I don't want to interfere with any plans you may have made, I should very much like you to join us there as my associate. I would want you to take charge of the surgical clinics. Use your own methods. All I want in return is results."

Will could hardly believe his ears. He had hoped for sympathetic understanding, but he had not dared hope he would be given a chance to prove Koch's theories in one of

New York's new hospitals where the eyes of the medical world would be on him and his work. There was no doubt in his mind about accepting the offer, but Sands, misunderstanding his hesitation, went on.

"Our surgical work at Roosevelt should interest you. A few years ago the trustees erected two frame cottages in the gardens to accommodate cases of erysipelas or any other infectious disease. One of the results has been to reduce the death rate from about ten percent to eight per cent. Perhaps the theory you have brought back may reduce it still further."

Will rose and shook the older man's hand. "Thank you, Henry, for your faith in me. I'll do my best."

They walked out of the office together. "Remember, Will, no compromise," Sands warned. "If you want to prove something, there must be no loopholes. You'll have plenty of criticism, and many difficult decisions to make, but, I repeat, no loopholes if you want real proof."

Dr. Sands was as good as his word, and Will, at twenty-eight, was appointed Associate Attending Surgeon. He had been to Roosevelt as a student at the College of Physicians and Surgeons, and he remembered well his first glimpse of it during his wanderings over the area before he entered the college. With its towers and minarets it still reminded him of pictures of the Kremlin he had seen in geography books. Its ornateness was in rather absurd contrast to the barren land north of Fifty-ninth Street inhabited only by squatters in crudely built shanties. Whatever it looked like, Will knew it represented a chance for real experimenting.

In a few weeks he gathered around him a group of young surgeons and a few older men sympathetic to his theories. Soon he was working long hours every day, performing operations of every kind. Instruments and the hands and arms of the operators were thoroughly washed in carbolic acid solution—carbolized water, it was called. White aprons were substituted for the usual black ones, and they were carefully changed after each operation. There was a good deal of murmuring among the nurses—as there had been at Bellevue —at Will's insistence upon frequent washing and changing of clothes, but Sands had said there must be no loopholes. Nurses who objected were put to work in some other operating room in the hospital, and several young doctors were dismissed for persistent neglect of their hands. Will's eagle eye was on every movement in his operating room.

The first test of his theories was, of course, the reduction in the number of patients who died under the surgeon's knife. Occasionally there would be some extremely difficult operation, but generally the surgeon was faced with routine cases similar to those performed in other operating rooms in Roosevelt or in other hospitals such as Bellevue or New York, so that a comparison of the death rates was not hard to make. Will noted carefully, as the months went by, that the rate in his clinic was lower than in any other, but he was quite aware that the difference was not yet great enough to be positive proof. The skill of the various surgeons was still an important factor. There were still loopholes.

One of the older surgeons in the hospital—Dr. Borridine, a man with many more years of experience than Will— frequently operated at the clinic. His skill was well known, and Will often turned over the more difficult cases to him. He had become accustomed to watching the younger men and the nurses carefully, but he had instinctively felt that he could relax a little when Borridine took over.

One day he was watching while Borridine was preparing for a bladder operation. Will's practiced eye went over the scene through force of habit. The patient lay quietly under the first effects of the ether; the white-robed nurses and assistants were in their proper places around the operating table. As Borridine prepared to make the first incision, all the tense, white-capped figures instinctively leaned forward. The surgeon laid a hand on the sheeted figure, and brought his scalpel over the bared abdomen. The fingers on the sheet were thin and capable, but Will's eyes saw something that made him catch his breath. In the corners of the nails were dark shadows. The nails were cut and trimmed, but the cuticles had obviously been neglected. Will remembered the infinitely small germs that he had seen in a tiny drop of blood through Koch's microscope. He knew what deadly danger lay in even one small particle of dirt. In a split second the operation would be under way. With the first incision of the surgeon's knife, the blood of the patient would be exposed to the bacilli lying hidden in the dirt in the corners of Borridine's fingernails. Sands had said there must be no loopholes. He had said nothing about exceptions. Dr. Borridine was Will's superior in age and experience. As operating surgeon he was, like the captain of a ship, in full charge. To Will, however, there were more important things to be considered. Not only was the success of Dr. Koch's germ theory at stake, but a man's life.

The scalpel hung over the helpless surface as the surgeon made his last-second calculation of the area to be cut; the white figures leaned in a circle like curling lily petals. The distant ticking of a clock was the only sound in the breathlessly silent room.

"Dr. Borridine." Will's voice was quiet, lest a sudden loud word cause a downward movement of the scalpel. Dr. Borridine held his position as though he didn't quite believe the interruption had taken place, but his eyes turned up to meet Will's. The white lily petals opened. Six startled faces under their white caps turned and stared.

"Your nails, Doctor," Will went on.

"Yes?" Borridine's eyes were still on Will, but between

them and his white cap was an irritated crease. It was no
moment for professional tact. The patient on the table was
all-important, and every second was immeasurably valuable.

"There is dirt in the nails," Will said bluntly. "We cannot
afford any chance of infection." As he spoke he moved to
Borridine's side and held out his own hand, palm down. The
nails were short and showed five immaculate crescents of
creamy white. The color rose in Borridine's face as Will
turned his hand palm up in a gesture that said as plainly as
words, "Give me the scalpel."

The anger in the older man's face was clear, but he was a
trained doctor. Four hundred and fifty years before Christ
a great Greek physician named Hippocrates had insisted
that doctors must suppress all personal feelings. This had
become part of the doctors' code through the ages, and the
so-called Hippocratic oath was required of all practicing
physicians. Dr. Borridine motioned to one of his assistants to
give Dr. Halsted a clean scalpel. The lily petals opened to
let him out of the circle, and immediately closed as the
younger surgeon leaned over and made the first incision.
Whether or not it would prove anything positive, there
would be no compromise in this operation.

Chapter
10

AN HOUR LATER THE OPERATING-ROOM DOOR WAS CLOSED gently by an assistant who asked if there was anything else he could do—and there was hesitation in his voice, as though he would like to say more or to ask Will another question. He had seen with his own eyes a young doctor stop an older surgeon about to perform an operation. This was unheard of in any hospital and it bewildered him, but after the slightest pause he said simply "Good night, Dr. Halsted," and left Will to his own thoughts.

It was the last operation for the day and Will was tired. He realized the enormity of what he had done, but he felt no regret. Von Volkmann had warned him that the value of asepsis would be difficult to prove. Will remembered his words: "Habits of a century are hard to break down, but I'm counting on you." Von Volkmann's faith in him, together with his own convictions, formed a double shield against any regret. He must, however, be prepared to face the immediate results of his action. Perhaps it would mean expulsion from the hospital, perhaps even a suspension of his license to practice. It was important for him to have friends sympathetic to his germ theories, and it was not unlikely that such a move as correcting an older surgeon during an operation would lose him sympathizers. Whatever might happen, he must be prepared to meet it.

He knew he must see Dr. Borridine as soon as possible.
It was not a question of offering an apology, but he felt he
must try to make the older man understand. As one of the
senior members of the staff, Dr. Borridine had a combina-
tion office and laboratory on the floor below the operating
room. Will paused a moment outside. A dim light was showing under the door, and he heard the opening and shutting
of a drawer. Will knocked. Borridine opened the door. With
no show of surprise he motioned Will to a chair.

"I had a feeling that you might come here," he said as
he seated himself at his desk. "I trust the operation was a
success?"

Borridine spoke without sarcasm, but there was a slight
challenge in his tone.

"Dr. Borridine," Will answered, "I don't believe you quite
understand. I—"

"On the contrary," the older doctor interrupted, "I understand perfectly. You are young and you have a theory.
Being young, you have let that theory possess you. The
history of medicine is largely a history of discarded theories.
In dealing with the unknown a man is very apt to let his
imagination run away with him."

Will had to interrupt here. "Dr. Borridine, I have seen
germs with my own eyes. They are not imagined."

Borridine made a gesture of impatience. "There is life
everywhere, my young enthusiast. Open a body to the air—
expose the insides of a human being—and you are bound to
get infection. Lister says to use carbolic acid. You say to
wash, wash, wash." He shrugged his shoulders. "There is
no avoiding possible death when you break into a human
body. You must expect pain—and often death. Remember,
there are diseases with which the medical profession is not
yet familiar. But," he added, "we do save many lives."

"But not enough, Doctor," Will protested. "I grant you

that some deaths result from diseases as yet unknown, but there is no reason at all why any life should be lost when the diagnosis is known to the surgeon. All I'm trying to do is to find out why even one life should be lost on the operating table."

Dr. Borridine pushed his chair back from the desk and stood up. It was clear that the interview was over. "I admire your energy, Halsted, and your ambition. Bring me real proof of your theories, and we will talk again. Until then I suggest that you follow accepted surgical practice. You might be endangering life rather than saving it." He held out his hand, but Will felt that the gesture meant nothing except perhaps that an older man was forgiving a younger one for a bit of rudeness.

Will lay awake most of that night. It would be morning before he could know anything about the patient's condition and whether or not the operation showed signs of being a success. If it turned out successfully and the patient recovered without any infection, he would be satisfied about the correctness of his theories even though Borridine continued to oppose them. If, on the other hand, the patient should become infected or die, Will would have to shoulder all responsibility while still having faith in his theories of cleanliness and general asepsis. He dozed off, but his dreams were restless and confused.

The news at the hospital the next morning was not good The patient had had a high fever all night. Pus was appearing around the edges of the wound, and there were indications that a deadly infection was setting in that might continue for weeks and then end fatally. Will felt very much alone. Even the fact that all the young doctors present at the operation were sympathetic to his ideas and methods, did not help. There was hostility in the air. He felt it as he leaned over and examined the sick man; he felt it when he straightened up and caught the eyes of the attending nurse and intern. Whatever he did, he was on his own. His problem was very clear in his mind. There must be some way in which germs could enter the blood stream in spite of carbolic acid and clean hands and instruments. As long as they did, and as long as patients died after operations, all the Borridines in the world would continue to think they were right.

He reopened the wound. His hands had never worked so methodically and so gently. The infection had not spread too deeply, but seemed to be centered about the catgut threads that had been used to sew up the wound. In one or two places the thread had cut into the tissues, and Will noticed that the greatest infection was at these points. He carefully cleaned the wound, scraping away the infected granulations. Then an idea flashed into his mind, the inspiration that often comes with great emergencies. Where the tissue was uninjured there was absolutely no sign of infection. Could the tissues be a natural protection against germs? Could the Creator have covered the organs of man with this thin but unbelievably tough material as a permanent protection? Otherwise, he asked himself, why was it so tough? When it was broken down, germs apparently flourished. He began to stitch the cleaned tissues, using silk thread instead of the catgut. His hands moved delicately and with the smoothness and accuracy of a fine piece of machinery, but his mind was on other things. He went over each step in the recent operation. There had been no slip-up anywhere, except the catgut ligatures— But this was standard practice. Might not the damaged tissues be another of the loopholes that old Dr. Sands had warned him about? This damage must be repaired. He matched the raw edges as an expert tailor would match the sides of a torn piece of material—the tissues must be restored to their original condition. When he was through, he turned the patient over to the attending nurse with careful instructions. He felt that this man and his fate had suddenly become terribly important not only to him but to the whole future of surgery.

Will went straight from the operating room to Dr. Sands' office. He certainly owed him some explanation. He found the doctor busy with another man; but as soon as he saw Will, Sands rose and came around his desk to greet him.

"Come in, Will, and sit down. This is Dr. Welch. I believe you two have met."

The doctor rose and shook hands. "Yes, Halsted, I think we spoke together before you went abroad two years ago. It's good to see you again. Sands here has been telling me about the theories you brought back. We have a lot to learn from Europe."

Soon the three doctors were in a deep discussion of Koch, Lister, and the new approach to surgery. Will told them of his recent experience with Borridine and the condition of the patient. He outlined his new idea about the possibility of infection from broken tissue and catgut. He was a little fearful of what they would think.

"Borridine's definitely difficult," Sands said when Will was through. He rose and walked slowly about as he talked. "I feel that you were quite justified in what you did, but it hasn't made things any easier. As for the tissue idea, it makes a lot of sense, eh, Welch?"

Welch nodded.

Sands paused before an old print of an operation in the Middle Ages. "Can't you imagine the torn tissues when those barber-surgeons plunged their hands into the poor patient? No wonder so few survived." He sat down at his desk again. "Sound though this idea may be, Roosevelt Hospital is full of doctors who will disagree with us. They have influence and they can't be persuaded overnight."

"Would it be possible," Will broke in, "to find a hospital

where I could try out all this without any interference?"

There was a silence that was finally broken by Dr. Welch. "I could have you appointed Visiting Physician at Bellevue," he said in a tone that gave Will the feeling that this suggestion was the result of some previous talk with Dr. Sands. "Perhaps, once there, you could speak to the trustees. I'll back you up."

This was the hospital where he had worked as an intern, and such a friendly, encouraging smile accompanied the offer that Will accepted at once. It meant doubling his work, but it was more than he had hoped for and he had never been one to shy away from work. He wanted an answer and here was a chance to find it. The future prospects were bright.

The trustees at Bellevue, however, proved to be harder to persuade than either Will or Dr. Welch had anticipated. Whatever they may have thought of germ and tissue theories, they objected to the whole proposition on the ground that there was no room in the hospital for such special work, certainly not enough money to build a separate operating theater.

Dr. Welch passed this discouraging news on to Will as the two men sat in Welch's office at Bellevue a week later.

"So I'm afraid that's it," Welch said, throwing up his hands in a gesture of despair. "I'm sorry, Halsted. You see, they're a stubborn bunch."

There was silence as Will thought over this blow to his hopes. The patient he had taken from Dr. Borridine at Roosevelt had completely recovered. That was an undeniable fact. Will was convinced that it was because of the repaired tissue and the use of silk ligatures. Dr. Borridine, on the other hand, put it down to sheer luck, and still remained unconvinced. Now another chance for proof was denied him. He broke the silence by pointing out the window and asking Dr. Welch a question.

"What do they use that courtyard for?"

From Welch's office could be seen two wings of the hospital separated by a small paved courtyard. Beyond were the main grounds with a few trees, and benches for the patients.

"It's really just an air space," Welch answered. "It is used as a short cut from one side of the hospital to the other. Why do you ask?"

"I was just thinking"—he spoke slowly and thoughtfully—"that if the trustees would agree to putting up a canvas shelter, or a tent, it would be accessible from the whole hospital, and yet would not really be an additional building. There would be room around it for passing from one wing to the other, so it would not interfere with present arrangements."

Dr. Welch smiled. "I said the trustees were a stubborn bunch, but you've certainly got a streak of obstinacy yourself. What makes you think the trustees will be willing to raise money even for a tent?"

"I won't ask them." Will's voice was getting more and more determined. "All I shall ask for is permission to build it. I'll take care of the rest myself."

Perhaps the trustees were so used to being asked for money that, when funds were not requested, they were surprised into granting permission to build. At any rate they agreed, and Will had the open space for his tent. As for the financing, he and his brother Richard and several friends supplied the necessary funds. An architect friend designed the tent, and in a very few weeks the open space in front of Dr. Welch's office was no longer open, but contained the first operating tent in New York. For centuries, operations had been performed in tents during wartime. Dirt, pain, horror, and death had filled them. Will's tent was different.

It was circular and almost filled the courtyard. On the sides nearest the wings of the hospital were canvas-covered passages through which patients were wheeled from the wards. Light during the day came through large portholes around the sides; gas for dark days and night operations was piped in from the hospital, as was both the hot and cold water. The floor was made of maple boards and set on edge as in bowling alleys. This was Will's own idea as he was an expert bowler and knew how firm and long-lasting were the floors of bowling alleys. Around the big pole in the center of the tent was a drainage ditch toward which the floor sloped. No army ever had an operating tent like this one, and Will was proud of it.

Even before the tent was finished, Will went to Dr. Borridine. His greeting was a little like that of a father to a son who has been naughty. This time, however, Will was not fearful, but was prepared to take the situation in hand.

"Dr. Borridine," he began when they were seated, "I remember you told me a short time ago that when I had proof of my theories of aseptic surgery, you would be glad to talk them over with me."

"I believe I did," the doctor agreed. "I shall listen with interest."

"I want you to do more than listen, Dr. Borridine," Will said quickly. "If you are willing, I should like you to do something."

"Yes?" Borridine asked, in the same tone he had used when Will interrupted him a month before at the operating table.

"I believe I am correct," Will continued, "in saying that the last three bladder operations you performed have resulted in serious infection."

"Young man . . ." Dr. Borridine began, in a hurt tone.

"Don't misunderstand me," Will added quickly. He sensed the irritation Borridine felt at being rebuked by a younger man. "Not for one moment do I question the skill with which the operations were performed. You have, Doctor, a reputation in surgery that I envy. What I do question are the conditions under which the operations were performed."

"So you have said before, Halsted; but that's not proof."

"I'm coming to that," Will went on. "At Bellevue we have a special operating room. You probably know of it." Borridine nodded as Will continued. "I am in complete charge. Every step in every operation must be done according to my orders."

Borridine was listening intently. He did not interrupt again.

"Would you be willing, Dr. Borridine, to perform the next three similar operations in my tent and entirely under my conditions? If all three are successful, you will have your proof. If not—well, we will be no worse off than we are now."

The older man raised his head and looked at Will in astonishment. He was about to speak, thought better of it, and turned his eyes away thoughtfully. There was a silence. A fly walked uninterruptedly across his hand, resting on the chair arm. His eyes moved unseeingly from one object to another in the office. Finally he turned to Will.

"And if I refuse?"

"That is your privilege," Will replied, "but remember that you asked for proof. I am merely asking you to supply that proof yourself. Isn't the future of surgery worth at least a try?"

There was no youthful arrogance in Will's voice. It was more a plea from one surgeon to another.

Dr. Borridine sensed this. When Will had interrupted

him at the operating table, he had suppressed his natural
anger and withdrawn quietly. Here was another challenge.
As in the first instance, his better nature prevailed. He
nodded agreement.

The first case came about a week later, followed in a few
days by a second. Will laid down very strict rules about general cleanliness, care of the tissues, and gentle ligaturing
with silk thread. Dr. Borridine followed the instructions
to the letter. His skill was unquestionable. Both patients recovered without a trace of infection.

The third case did not come for some time. Will deliberately avoided talking with Borridine. It must be a perfect
experiment without a trace of prejudice. Two weeks went by
and Will found himself watching the third operation. From
the first incision to the final closing of the wound, not a
movement of Borridine's hands escaped his notice. One small
deviation from the rules of procedure, deliberate or otherwise, could invalidate the proof Will sought. The patient
was moved back to the ward, and the period of waiting
began.

The first day there was a slight fever, and Will paced the
anteroom of the ward all night. The next day the fever
had dropped. The third day Will had to perform several
emergency operations. They proved rather a relief to his
nerves. When he had completed the last one, he hurried
back to the ward. As he approached it, the door opened
and Borridine stepped out. Their eyes met and Will's were
full of questioning.

The answer lay behind the door. It was to be found in
the condition of an unknown man lying on a bed—a man
who did not realize that he might be the instrument for
bringing about a revolution in surgery. Will was about to
ask Dr. Borridine the simple, straightforward question, but
the older surgeon anticipated him. Taking Will by the arm,

he led him a few steps from the door. He had to make an effort to say what he said, but there was no doubt of his sincerity.

"Halsted, I owe you an apology. There is no longer any trace of infection. The granulation is healthy. Go in and see for yourself." He put his hand on Will's shoulder with a reassuring pressure and started down the hall. As Will opened the door of the ward, Borridine paused and turned suddenly.

"Halsted," he called quietly, "you can count on me from now on."

Chapter

11

THE VICTORY OVER DR. BORRIDINE WAS NO PERSONAL TRIUMPH for Will Halsted. The older surgeon had a large following not only at Roosevelt Hospital but at other hospitals throughout the city. His admission of the extreme value of surgical asepsis would be accepted by almost all of them.

Will couldn't help thinking back to his college days when a game was won not by one man alone but by the cooperation of the whole team. In surgery the team had been a large one. First and foremost there was little Dr. Koch. Then there was Dr. von Volkmann himself, as well as Sands and Welch and all the young doctors who had believed in him and given him courage to go on. They were the ones he counted on. They were the future surgeons of America. Nothing must interfere with their training in the new methods.

With this idea in mind Will organized classes of his own. Many of them were held in his house on Twenty-fifth Street, but most of them in the wards and sick rooms of all the New York hospitals. Will was a familiar figure in all of them, spending his mornings at the outpatient department of the Roosevelt Hospital and being on constant day and night call at the others. In spite of all this work and his regular teaching in the dissecting room of his old college, he found time for the sixty or more young men who attended his special

106

classes. These young surgeons soon caught Will's enthusiasm. They admired his skill and his perseverance in the face of persistent criticism from many doctors. His painstaking care in the handling of tissues was something that none of them had ever before witnessed. The emphasis was no longer on speed in an operation. Will insisted on deliberate perfection in every move. His reputation as a teacher spread and places in his classes were eagerly sought.

He had very little time for his family or for social activities. His friends often asked him why he didn't marry. He always smiled and replied that there would be time for that later, but just now he was too busy. His sister Minnie was living in Albany, and his father and mother seldom saw him. His father's aloofness was a constant worry. Will felt pretty sure that the older man was at least partly reconciled to his not being in the business; but what he longed for was some admission from his father of pride in what he was doing, especially as his theories were beginning to be recognized among American surgeons.

The hospitals were still plagued by various infections following operations and wound-dressings. However, there was a definite lessening of the death rate from infection. Books were appearing explaining the value of asepsis. They pointed out how lack of care, exposure, and moist air made animal and vegetable matter decay and how, in decay, dangerous bacteria flourished and brought infection.

In the summer of 1881 Will was pleased to be appointed to the Chambers Street Hospital. This emergency hospital, with the most active surgical service, was situated in the shipping district south of Canal Street, very near the docks. A saloon owned by Steve Brody, the man who jumped from the Brooklyn Bridge on a dare, was just around the corner. The hospital was open night and day to receive accident cases and treat them free of charge. The patients were poor.

They were tough. Most of them were ignorant. Almost every race from the Orient and the Pacific as well as from the Latin nations along the Mediterranean was represented. Many could hardly speak English well enough to ask for help. Their injuries resulted from family quarrels, street fights, attempted murder. They were brought in at the rate of fourteen or fifteen a night, chiefly between two and four in the morning, and all received fair and equal treatment.

It was known as the House of Relief and was an old brownstone English basement dwelling. Will was greatly disturbed when he looked over the equipment on his arrival. It was not of the best, not up to his standards. The operating room was small and the patients followed each other so closely that the work had to be done fast, not allowing much time for the extreme care that he was used to. Gauze bandages were a luxury. Most of the dressings were made from pieces torn from a roll of bleached muslin. Coarse catgut ligatures, which Will had given up, were used. When the wound was small, hairs pulled from the tails of the ambulance horses took the place of the coarse catgut. Will was amazed that, under these conditions, so many lives were saved. Possibly, he thought, the rough existence led by these men and women built up an unusual resistance to germs.

In those days the boats that plied the Sound and the Hudson River were lighted by gas. Many of the patients— passengers or crewmen—brought into the Chambers Street Hospital suffered from gas poisoning. This was illuminating gas or, as it was known to the doctors, carbon monoxide. When it got into the blood it replaced the life-giving oxygen that the blood contained, and the patient died for want of air.

Will watched the doctors treat the patients by letting them bleed in order to get rid of the poisonous blood. Needless death was something he had dedicated himself to prevent, and here was another challenge. He gave it a great deal of thought, and one evening he asked Dr. Bull, the chief surgeon, if he might try an experiment on the next severe case of gas poisoning. Dr. Bull looked at Will and smiled. He knew very well that he was faced by a young man who would never take No for an answer without putting up an argument. He knew of the Borridine incident, and how right Will had been in spite of all the criticism.

"Well, Halsted," he said, "I have a feeling that, if I don't give you permission, you will find some way of gaining your point. Just what do you propose?"

"I reason this way," Will explained. "The practice now is to let the poisoned blood out of the patient, and with it the suffocating carbon-monoxide gas. This is all very well if a man is strong—he is able to withstand the loss of blood until the body can repair the damage. On the other hand, if the poisoning is very severe or if the patient is not in the very best of health, the strain on the heart from this lack of blood is too great for the body to bear."

"And so?" Dr. Bull asked.

"If there were some way of replacing the carbon-monoxide with healthy oxygen from the air, the blood could return to its original state."

"And you know of some way?"

"I never say I know, Doctor," Will answered simply. "But what I propose is to remove a large part of the patient's blood—say, three or four pints—mix it with the oxygen of the air, and return it to the blood stream."

Dr. Bull was unbelieving. This had never been done. For centuries, blood had been taken out of a person's body to relieve pressure—bloodletting, it was called—but never had it been suggested that the blood be put back. If anyone other than Will Halsted had proposed it, his answer would have been a definite No but, after only a moment's thought, he promised to give Will full charge of the next severe case of gas poisoning.

A few days later, around three in the morning, the little horse-drawn ambulance brought in a crewman from a Hudson River night boat who had fallen asleep near a leaky gas pipe. They laid him gently on a cot and turned him over to Will. The blue-gray skin, the irregular snorelike breathing, the weak heartbeat, and the expression of pain at every breath told Will, even before he heard the report, that this was the challenge he had asked for. Seconds were precious, but he had been ready ever since his talk with Dr. Bull.

A tourniquet was applied to shut off the return flow of blood to the heart. Four full pints of blood were drawn from the veins. Here Will knew he was on dangerous ground. Too much blood withdrawn would prove fatal to the patient. He knew that it must be replaced quickly. The blood was placed in a jar with a solution of salt to keep it in liquid form, and thoroughly shaken. Time ticked warningly away on the clock. With every second the patient on the cot became weaker. Will knew that all eyes were on him. Speed alone would prevent the blood from becoming solid and useless. Now came the peak moment of his experiment. The blood, purified by shaking, must be returned to the fragile body. It could not be returned to the veins; the flow there was too slow, and it must reach every part of the body as soon as possible. Will filled a large syringe, opened an artery and, working with desperate speed, drove the blood against the stream coming from the heart until the syringe was empty.

A minute passed and then another. The blue-gray face was very near to his own as Will leaned over listening to the labored breathing. The life or death result would be evident in a matter of minutes. Will was quite used to crises on the operating table, but this stranger had not asked for what Will had done. He had been given no choice. Will watched and listened, his own heart beating fast. Five minutes after he had closed the artery, the breathing became quieter and more regular. This meant only one thing. Healthy blood was seeping into the lungs and replacing the poison. The eyelids quivered and Will knew the man would live.

He stepped away from the cot. He had thought fast and worked fast. The strain on his nerves had been great and he was ready to rest. The schedule at Chambers did not allow much time for relaxation; but he hurried to the little room he shared with another doctor, and threw himself down on his bed. He let his eyes close, and for a few seconds he was blissfully unconscious. Then he felt himself being shaken. He heard a voice and, rubbing his eyes, he sat up.

"Western Union has just sent over this wire, Doctor."

Will took the piece of yellow paper from the orderly, and read the message:

MINNIE VERY ILL HEMORRHAGE CAN YOU COME AT ONCE

It was from Albany and was signed SAM. What a tragic coincidence! First an unknown man, his blood poisoned by a leaky gas pipe. Then his own sister, a hundred and eighty miles away, losing her blood by a hemorrhage.

Dr. Bull was most co-operative and sent Will to the railroad terminal at Forty-second Street in one of the hospital's horse-drawn ambulances. Will dozed beside the driver, who woke him up with a prod of his whip when they reached the station. There was some unexplained delay before the train got under way, and a half-hour wait at Poughkeepsie for the Albany connection.

Finally the train pulled in, and a little after one o'clock he was at Minnie's bedside. Following the birth of her baby she had suffered a severe hemorrhage and was losing blood as a broken dam would lose water. Sam and the nurse had staunched the bleeding with gauze and muslin packing, much as the break in the dam would be stuffed with sandbags. The bleeding had somewhat lessened; but she was desperately weak, and her pulse was only a slight flutter. For the second time that day, Will realized that only heroic action of some sort could save the patient for whom Fate had made him responsible.

Minnie needed blood to replace what she had lost, or her heart would stop beating. He had healthy blood. If he could get it into his sister's veins, they would carry it to her rapidly weakening heart. He knew the risk. Blood was something about which comparatively little was known, and he feared the unknown changes that might occur between his veins and his sister's. Her heart could not last much longer; the pulse was pitifully weak. It was a long chance, but he must take it. Stripping off his coat and rolling up his sleeves, he had Sam tie a tourniquet tightly about his upper arm. Piercing a vein in the crook, he drew off a pint of blood and gently forced it into his sister's veins. He repeated the operation. The seconds passed, as they had a few hours before in the gloomy room at Chambers Street Hospital. Once again, the miracle happened. Through his forefinger, held on her wrist, he felt the heartbeat strengthen. Regularity replaced the dying flutter. He let Sam feel it. The two men straightened up. They knew, and agreed with a silent look, that the crisis had been passed.

Leaving Minnie in the care of the nurse, they went into the next room and sat down. There was no need for Sam to speak his gratitude. He had seen Will perform successfully an experiment never done before without fatal results. They sat in silence while Will closed his eyes and rested.

"There is something you ought to know, Will," Sam said finally.

Will opened his eyes and turned his head questioningly.

"When I realized how serious Minnie's condition was, I

telegraphed your father. I thought he would want to come right up. Apparently he couldn't get away. Instead, he wired me. Here's the message." He handed it to Will. It was very brief, but it said far more to Will than twice as many words could have done.

SEND FOR MY SON WILL HALSTED AT ONCE. WILLIAM M. HALSTED.

It made Will forget his weariness.

Chapter
12

THE LOSS OF TWO PINTS OF BLOOD AND THE WORRY OVER HIS
sister's condition had weakened even Will's strong constitu-
tion, and he decided to follow Sam's advice and take the
boat back to New York, instead of the train. The river trip
in the open air helped strengthen him.

When the boat docked, late in the evening, he went at
once to Chambers Street. It seemed dreary and shut in after
his day on the river boat, but it represented work and
accomplishment and he was glad to be back. His first
thought was of the man whose blood he had cleansed of gas.
Dr. Bull reassured him. The man had recovered more
quickly than had been expected and had been moved to
Bellevue before being sent home.

"But now," Dr. Bull continued, "I want to hear about your
sister."

Will gave him a detailed account of what he had done.

Dr. Bull shook his head silently before speaking. "You
have courage, Halsted. I don't believe such a thing has
been done for ten years. Even before you became a medical
student, doctors frowned on the practice. Blood clots too
easily. Too many patients died. I was amazed that you

were able to take so much from that man here and put it back."

"Of course I lost almost half of what I took out," Will admitted. "But I used a salt solution to keep the blood from clotting—and I worked fast."

Dr. Bull smiled. "Just the same, I wouldn't have thought it possible. And now your sister. To me it seems you have performed two miracles in the last twenty-four hours."

"Let's leave miracles to the Bible, Dr. Bull," Will replied, "and go back to the old proverb that necessity is the mother of invention. My sister was about to die. I had to do something."

Dr. Bull muttered a polite but not very convincing "True." He was convinced of only one thing. This young doctor had not only skill but imagination and courage.

Will gladly followed Dr. Bull's suggestion that he go home for the rest of the night. He couldn't deny that he was tired, and it was with a great sense of relief that he opened the door of his house. Dr. McBride, with whom he shared the house, was away, and the dark hall seemed very silent. He lighted the gas, and saw some mail that had been dropped through the slot in the door. He picked it up and was about to toss it on the hall table, to read in the morning, when one letter caught his eye. It had a foreign stamp and was addressed in the familiar handwriting of Richard von Volkmann. Lighting the lamp in the parlor, Will sat down to read it. It was quite long and contained much news of doctor friends in Europe. Von Volkmann was enthusiastic about the work that Will was doing in surgery. He had, he said, been keeping himself informed about the activities of his young American friend. The letter ended with an invitation:

". . . The German Surgical Association is meeting in Frankfort next month. I intend to put your name up for membership. You must not refuse me. You will be welcome

at our home for as long as you care to stay. We shall have
much to talk about.

Your friend,

RICHARD VON VOLKMANN

Will lighted a cigarette and lay back in his chair. As the
smoke drifted up into the darkness above the dim lamp, he
enjoyed a few minutes of self-satisfaction—a warm, com-
fortable feeling of work well done. His victory over Borridine had brought him recognition and sympathy from doctors and students alike. The possibilities in surgery for him
seemed limitless. He smiled at the thought that he was
barely thirty-two years old, and the letter in his hand held
an offer of recognition by a foreign surgical group at the request of one of the greatest of European surgeons.

A disturbing thought crept into his mind. Next month his
classes would start again for the winter. How could he go
off to Europe for purely personal reasons? He carried this
question to bed with him, hoping to have found an answer
by morning.

The next day his mind was no clearer on the subject. He
needed someone else's opinion, and who better than Doctor
Welch? Ever since they had met, Will had found him a
kindred spirit. On his way down to Chambers Street he
stopped at Bellevue Hospital.

Dr. Welch read Von Volkmann's letter, and then spoke
to Will with a little surprise in his voice. "I can't see that this
presents any need for advice. It's a wonderful opportunity
and a great compliment."

"But," Will reminded him, "my classes start again next
month. I can't give them up."

"It's not a question of giving up anything," Welch answered. "It's very flattering to the class to have you honored
in this way."

"I'm not sure that even *you* know how much the group means to me," Will said.

"I know you've done a fine job of teaching, Will," the older doctor answered. "You've somehow managed to instill in every one of your students the same sense of excitement—of adventure—that you yourself feel about each new problem and each new patient."

"Thanks," Will said, smiling in embarrassment. He pulled at his mustache thoughtfully as he tried to find the words that would express what he was thinking. "I've been out of Med. for how long now—five, six years? I'm the youngest member of the staff here. Yet already I seem to have managed to antagonize every other doctor on the staff. I've tried to get my theories into print. Nothing doing. Polite regrets or no reply at all. The words 'antisepsis' and 'germs' seem to be poison to editors and doctors everywhere."

"You're too impatient, Will. These things take—"

"Time. I know. But there's a short cut. If I can persuade my students to adopt my theories as well as my methods—if I can convince them to give as much loving care to the handling of tissues and membranes as a tailor gives when he works on beautiful material—then they'll save lives. And the next time a patient comes in with a similar wound, he'll ask for one of my boys. And so the word will spread."

Dr. Welch smiled and put an arm around Will's shoulders.

"I think it *will* work," he said. "But it's hardly the way for you to build a name for yourself, Will."

"A name!" Will exclaimed. "Who cares about a name? You can't eat it. A name never helped a man to sleep better. I've discovered that the most effective sedative in the world is the knowledge that you're saving lives."

"I am sure," Dr. Welch said, "that Dr. Hall can be counted on to take over; but if it will make it any easier for you to decide, I will personally supervise your classes while you are away."

That settled it in Will's mind, and so it was arranged. He wrote to Von Volkmann accepting his invitation, and secured passage on the S.S. *Campania*. Two weeks later he found himself in Halle enjoying the hospitality of the Von Volkmanns. The meeting at Frankfurt was several days off and the two doctors had a great deal to talk about. It was not all on the subject of surgery. Von Volkmann, besides being a great surgeon, was a poet, with all the poet's fondness for the beautiful. Will liked music and had the collector's love of old places and things. The little town of Halle had much to offer both doctors. It was full of picturesque old buildings, each with its legend. Bach for twenty years was organist of the Market Church. Goethe, the German poet, wrote here, and Martin Luther preached Protestantism in the shadow of the Archbishop's residence.

One evening they attended a concert given by the Handel Society, and walked home by moonlight. The slender twin spires of the Marian church, cutting through the face of the moon, inspired Von Volkmann to quote the poet Wordsworth, " 'Spires whose slender finger points to Heaven.' " Then he added, "I've always liked to think of ambition when I hear that quotation. Always pointing up to greater things. You have it, my young friend. Never let it go."

On the day of the meeting, as he looked around, Will recognized many of the men he had met on his first trip, when he was just out of medical school. The meeting was interesting. Will listened to papers on various phases of surgical practice, and to the discussions that followed each. He loved a good argument, and found it hard not to speak up when things were said with which he didn't agree; but he was only a visitor, and discussion was limited to members.

As the chairman rapped his gavel to end the discussion of the final paper, Von Volkmann rose and requested permission to speak. He then addressed the chairman. "Mr. Chairman, I should like to propose the name of an American colleague and friend for membership in this organization. Dr. William Stewart Halsted is young in years, but he has already proved his skill, courage, and imagination. He brought the theories of Koch and Lister to his own country, and through his persistent efforts aseptic surgery is largely accepted there. I know of no one more capable of contributing to the ideals of this organization."

When he sat down, Dr. Von Strolzheim rose and seconded the nomination. As Will had been told, the final election was a matter for a meeting of the directors, but the kind words Von Volkmann had spoken publicly were worth more to Will than any election. The two exchanged a smile as the meeting went on to other business.

Before Will left Frankfurt, Von Volkmann asked him if he would be interested in going on to Heidelberg, where the Congress of Eye Surgeons was holding a meeting. He had been told, he said, that a friend of his, Dr. Carl Koller, an intern at Allgemeine Krankhaus in Vienna, was to make a report on some rather unusual experiment. Will agreed, little knowing the final results of his apparently unimportant decision.

Heidelberg was crowded. The annual Ophthalmic Congress attracted not only those who practiced eye surgery but doctors and surgeons in general practice. Of course, the rumor that Koller had something remarkable to say had much to do with attracting the curious. The Town Hall was packed to the doors, but Von Volkmann's friendship for Koller and his own great reputation secured him and Halsted seats near the platform.

About halfway through the proceedings a Dr. Brettauer of

Trieste was introduced. He told the assembled doctors that he regretted that Dr. Koller was unable to be present himself, but that he had asked him to make a few remarks and conduct an experiment. He then explained that Dr. Koller had recently become aware of the anesthetic properties of cocaine when he took some in his mouth and found that it made his tongue and lips numb. He reminded the audience that this drug had been known ever since 1860, when Dr. Albert Nieman, assistant to Woehler, had isolated the powerful alkaloid from the South American coca leaves and named it cocaine. The important thing, Dr. Brettauer pointed out, was that Dr. Koller not only had become aware of this anesthetic but had put it to use, as the Congress would shortly see for themselves.

The audience shifted in their seats and whispered to one another. Then followed a dramatic silence during which a dog was wheeled in strapped to a table. His lower jaw rested on a cushion and he was turned to face the crowd that was gaping at him. He was not strapped in a way to make him uncomfortable, for when Dr. Brettauer stroked his head he wagged his tail contentedly. Taking a dropper from a tray of instruments, Brettauer filled it with a measured amount of brownish liquid. Again stroking the dog's head, he gently let three drops fall on its left eye. There was only the slightest involuntary movement from the animal. A minute passed; then two minutes, and three. Dr. Brettauer took a pair of forceps from the tray and turned back to the dog. Everyone was leaning forward. He brought the forceps over the dog's eye. Though the right eye quivered slightly, the left remained motionless. The forceps touched the eyeball, closed on it, and raised it a fraction of an inch before releasing it. Any sound of pain or discomfort could easily have been heard in the silent room, but there was none. The crowd gasped, partly from disbelief and partly in relief. There was, though, still no sign from the dog.

The remainder of the meeting seemed dull after this demonstration. Will could not put out of his mind the picture of the patient dog undergoing what would ordinarily have been unbearable pain. His thoughts went back ten years to the little injured dog on the dark street in New Haven. It had cried out when he barely touched it. This juice of the strange coca shrub was indeed magic if it could deaden pain so quickly and so completely. Lister and Koch had fought a battle against germs, and Will had been their eager disciple. Now Koller with his cocaine was fighting against pain.

Will discussed the experiment with Von Volkmann on the way back to Halle. The German surgeon was not enthusiastic. In his own practice he used ether and chloroform, and he understood that eye doctors had consistently used an ether spray to freeze the eye during an operation. These, he felt, were most satisfactory.

"The demonstration was most dramatic," he admitted, "but to carry this almost unknown juice to the deeper nerves and blood vessels is too great a risk. How do we know what effect it will have on the whole of a patient's body?"

Will couldn't answer this question, and it wasn't his habit to make any statement without proof; so he let the matter drop. But he vowed to himself that he would follow it through. His goal would be not only clean but painless surgery.

Chapter

13

A WEEK LATER WILL'S SHIP STEAMED INTO NEW YORK HARBOR. His mind was full of speculations. He was confident that he was on the verge of a great discovery in surgery. Only a few years before, he had returned from Europe with ideas about germs and aseptic surgery. He had proved he was right then. Here was a chance to do it again. The gangplank scraped and banged down to the chorus of shouting deckhands. Will moved slowly toward it with the crowd. He was about to step off onto the dock, his mind filled with visions of the future, when he heard a familiar voice.

"Will! Will! Over here." Surprising as it was, there was no doubt about it—it was his father. He rushed through the crowd and grasped the older man's hand. "Dad!" he exclaimed. "What on earth are you doing here?" His father pulled him toward the exit as Will went on talking. "How did you know I was on this ship? I didn't tell a soul."

"Let's get a cab," was the only reply. "I'll answer your questions then."

Soon the cab was rattling off over the cobblestones, heading for Will's house on Twenty-fifth Street, and Will got his answer. It seemed that his mother, who for years had been ill with some unknown ailment, had suddenly taken a turn for the worse while visiting Minnie in Albany. His father hastened to explain that she was resting quietly at the moment, but the doctors were unable to account for the frequent recurrence of pain.

"What doctors have you talked to?" Will asked.

"Your friend Tom McBride is in charge," his father answered, "but we have called in Janeway, Sands, and Delafield."

Will was astonished. He knew all these men, and he knew they were the best in New York.

"I hoped for help from them, but they seemed quite in the dark." There was a slight, rather embarrassed pause. "I've decided that if your mother can be helped at all you are the one to do it. I cabled Von Volkmann and he told me what ship you were on. I want you to come and see her, Will. I want your opinion."

All thoughts of Koller and his coca juice were put aside. Will packed what he needed, and left at once for Albany with his father. He found his mother resting quietly. She smiled at him, and held his hand tightly and confidently as he told her briefly of his recent trip. He examined her carefully; he read the report of the other doctors and talked at great length with Tom McBride. The more he talked, the more fearful he became. His mother, without doubt, was seriously ill. She was slightly jaundiced, with tumefaction and great tenderness in the region of the gall bladder. His suspicions grew stronger and stronger. She was, he felt sure, suffering from an illness known and feared for hundreds of years. Hard substances, or calculi, popularly called "stones," were forming in a part of her body that supplied a fluid necessary to digestion. There was no known cure, and the "stones" would increase in number until she would be unable to eat. Their origin had been a complete mystery since before the time of Christ, and even as late as the middle of the century the cure was brutal cutting with agonizing pain. Even now, with anesthesia, Will knew that deaths from postoperative infection were common.

Only too soon the moment came when he must give his opinion to his father. The older Halsted knew little of medicine, and Will dreaded having to try to explain. It had to be done, and Will made it as simple as he could.

"I understand, Will," his father said when his son was through. "Now what do you propose to do?"

"Mother is resting now, which is good. I suggest that we give her another day of quiet. Then, with your permission, I shall operate. There is no accepted procedure because, as far as I know, no such operation has ever been deliberately planned, certainly not in this country. It's the only suggestion I can properly make. The symptoms are not too bad, and there is an excellent chance of success."

He tried to sleep when he went to his room, but found it impossible. He lay awake planning the operation as a general would plot a vital campaign. He was prepared to give his mother ether. At least she would be relieved of the torturing pain that had through the ages accompanied the removal of gallstones. He had the fleeting wish that he might use Koller's coca juice, but that would have to wait. One problem at a time. Tom McBride would be there to help him. The rest was in his own hands—skillful, nerveless hands that had never let him down. He had decided to make the incision above the sac where the stones were forming. This he knew was considered safe, but perhaps . . . He dozed off.

Suddenly he became conscious of his father's voice, and of a hand shaking his shoulder.

"Will—Will—wake up! Your mother is—"

In a minute Will was at his mother's bedside. She was in terrible pain. He glanced at the clock. It was two o'clock in the morning. Tom McBride had left for the night, and Sam

Vander Poel was away. He was alone, with only his father and his sister to help.

"It's all right, Mother."

Then he changed from the sympathetic son to the careful, confident surgeon. He gave quiet orders to Minnie and his father—boiling water, soap, clean sheets and towels, all the available lamps in the house. He laid out his instruments with precision—scalpel, forceps, clamps, needles already threaded for the final suturing. He chose Minnie to give the anesthetic. It required delicacy of touch and a calmness that he didn't feel his father had. His strong arms were not strained in placing his mother on the wooden table dragged from the kitchen into the parlor.

He handed Minnie a large piece of gauze, and instructed her to place it over their mother's mouth and nose. He took from his bag a vial of ether in solution.

"Drop by drop on the gauze," he told her. "When she is unconscious, keep it up at greater intervals but regularly. That is important. Make a rhythm of it. Think of some popular tune, and let a drop fall on every third beat."

He gave these orders without looking at Minnie. He knew that, as the wife of a doctor, she would hear and understand. The parlor was not the best of operating rooms, but he had to make the best of it.

He watched his mother's eyes close slowly. Her pulse and breathing were regular. The pain had made all her muscles tighten, but now they became relaxed in unconsciousness. He picked up the scalpel. His strokes were delicately sure, and in seconds the gall sac was exposed. It lay there as harmless-looking as a child's partly blown-up balloon. In reality, it contained poison and possible death.

The drops of ether were falling regularly on the gauze as Minnie hummed "The Old Oaken Bucket." The elder Halsted was handing his son the instruments. He occasionally

wiped his forehead with the back of his hand. He watched
every movement that his son made as a faithful dog watches
its master. The breathing of the four persons was the only
sound. It was a strange family gathering.

Will leaned over and cut into the sac. The ugly contents
soaked into the gauze packing. He carefully inserted his
fingers, cautiously feeling for what he was sure was there.
One by one he drew out seven small stones, dark and green-
ish. He laid them aside and reached for the first needle,
and with a few deft strokes closed the slit. Never had tissues
been handled so gently; never had a surgeon sutured a
wound with more skillful care. He motioned to Minnie to
remove the gauze. What surgery could do he had done. The
final decision was out of his hands. The pulse strengthened,
the eyelids fluttered, and there was a movement of the head.
He waited to be sure that this was not some involuntary
spasm. It was repeated as the eyelids opened. He felt confident that his mother would live.

Three days later he was sure enough of the success of the
operation to return to New York, and his father saw him off
on the train. Will felt how difficult it was for the older man
to express his gratitude after his years of indifference, and
he tried to make it easy for him by talking of other things.
Halfway through the station, his father took him by the arm
and pulled him to one side of the crowd.

"Will," he said, "I saw things the other night that I didn't
think possible. And you, Will—you did them. How miracles
are performed is one of God's mysteries. His instruments
are of His own choosing. I shall never question that again."
With a pressure of his hand on Will's arm, Mr. Halsted
turned and hurried through the crowd. Will smiled as he
boarded the train and sat back in his seat. He knew his
father had awarded him the accolade of his approval.

The six-hour trip to New York was to Will a restful pause between two experiments. The gallstone operation on his mother had been definitely an experiment. As he had told his father, there was no real authority for what he had done. He had operated through necessity, much as he had transfused blood into his sister's veins a year before. In both cases he had been successful. At the end of the six hours he would be faced with another experiment, the results of which he had no way of knowing.

He was still fascinated by the thought of using Koller's coca juice for deep operations. If a few drops on the outside of the eye of a dog could make the eye insensitive to pain, why would not an injection below the skin make that part of the body just as insensitive? It was a challenging idea but, just as in the case of Koch's germs, it was one that must be turned into fact before the world would believe. This was the task that Will silently assigned to himself.

He must, of course, have help, and he decided on his friend Richard Hall, who, he was sure, would be open-minded about any proposed advance in surgery. He had known Hall, who was a year younger, ever since medical school. Together they had performed the first appendix operation in New York. Though it had not been successful, Hall and the other doctors who followed the operation agreed with him that, in cases of general peritonitis, the appendix—the wormlike tube attached to the right side of the intestine—should be removed as soon as possible. His theory had proved correct in spite of the failure of his first experiment, and appendectomies had become common.

Back in New York, Will was not disappointed. Dick Hall was enthusiastic and full of suggestions, and brought several young doctors to their first conference. They decided to begin their experiments at one of their regular meetings in

Dr. Halsted's house. There would be twenty or thirty students besides themselves. "I want witnesses, and thirty should be plenty," Will had said.

The problem of getting the coca-leaf preparation was easily solved by the manager of the chemical firm of Parke, Davis and Company. He not only supplied them with a solution of the drug but also gave them a package of freshly imported leaves. He was quite excited about the new discovery, and anxious to talk about it.

Will led him on with questions. "These come from South America?" he asked.

"Yes," the manager answered. "It's a large shrub, about four to eight feet high, that grows in the mountains of Peru, Bolivia, and Colombia. The natives have used it for centuries."

"Peru's a long way off," Will remarked. "How did it ever get to Europe?"

"Missionaries and other travelers," was the answer. "They all reported that the native Indians used it to give them strength for hard work, or for long trips over the mountains. They chewed it constantly, and the result seems to have been that they never had a feeling of fatigue."

"But Koller in Germany?" Will persisted. "What put him on the trail of using it in an eye operation?"

"I'm told he tried chewing it, and found that it made his tongue sort of numb. Being an eye doctor, he first wondered what effect it would have on the cornea—and that was it."

"Is it soluble in water?" Sam asked.

"Oh, yes. Of course, as I said, the natives chewed the leaves. Now they are prepared by a slow boiling that leaves a sort of brown residue; when this dries and is dissolved in water, it yields a low-percentage solution. We are working on some way to refine it, so that the dried residue will be white; but I doubt if that will make any difference in its potency."

Will and Dick thanked him and went out with their precious material.

When the class met at his house some nights later, there was an air of excitement in Will's greeting which he could not suppress. The students sensed it, and a dramatic silence came over the group. Will explained briefly what was known of the new drug, and pointed out that there was as yet no definite knowledge of all its possibilities. He proposed to start experimenting by injecting a four per cent solution under the skin. He had determined upon this percentage almost at random, he said, as probably the strongest that was safe and the weakest that would give the desired effect. Of course, he added, further experience might easily justify a change in the strength of the solution. Since the results of such procedure were unknown, he would make the first injection on himself.

He took off his coat, rolled up his sleeve, and held his arm toward Dick Hall, who washed the forearm carefully with soap and carbolic acid. Will then picked up a small syringe and drew out about six drops of the solution. These were simple gestures, routine to all, but under the circumstances they took on special importance, and every eye was focused on Will and the harmless-looking liquid. As he always did in a clinical demonstration, Will explained exactly what he planned to do. He held the syringe upward over his arm as he spoke.

"I intend to inject this small dose just below the elbow on the upper side of my forearm. It will, as you know, enter the ulna nerve. As you also know—and I only say it as a reminder, in order that there will be no misunderstanding— this nerve begins near the armpit and extends to the distal end of the ulna bone at the wrist. I pick this nerve because it is easily accessible and any lessening of feeling will be most easily detected."

There was a tense silence as Will inserted the needle in his bare arm and forced the liquid out of the syringe. He withdrew the syringe and placed it on the table. Then he sat down, rested his arm on the table, and waited. After about two minutes he began feeling his left arm with his right hand, from his shoulder to his wrist. "I think," he said, "we have made at least one discovery. It seems evident from this experiment that the effect of the drug is downward from the point of injection. I have no feeling from just below my elbow to my wrist. Up to my shoulder everything seems to be normal. I would—" Will stopped. He felt a sudden dizziness, and his forehead broke out in a cold sweat. Several men stepped forward to help him. "It's to be expected," he said quietly, "but perhaps we'd better call it off until tomorrow night."

The students left, but Dick Hall stayed on. In an hour or so Will felt so much better that he sat up for several hours talking, in spite of Dick's efforts to get him to go to bed.

For the next several meetings they tried injections in various strengths in other nerves of the body—the sciatic in the region of the hip, the internal pubic which fed into the leg, and the whole brachial plexus that supplied the nerves for the breast and shoulder. The results in all cases were the same, and showed that the injected nerve was numb from the point of injection downward. Three or four of the students, as well as Dick, volunteered. In all cases there was a feeling of sickness and dizziness which, as Will had found that first night, soon wore off and left a feeling of well being that was very pleasant.

It was more than pleasant. It was exhilarating. It took the tiredness out of their muscles, and seemed to revitalize their eagerness for the work of the classes. The routine of their hospital duties was no longer a burden, and they sat up far into the night, arguing and discussing, their minds clear and retentive. They spoke of the cocaine as "Mama Coca," the name the Peruvian Indians used for it. They chewed the leaves, both fresh and dry, sometimes mixing them with lime. The taste they found fragrant and slightly bitter. They even snuffed the powdered residue up their nostrils after the custom of the gay young snuff takers of the eighteenth century.

Will realized that they had in their hands a most remarkable drug. Its numbing qualities might well provide a new anesthetic. But were the nerves that seemed numb actually insensible to pain? Were they really blocked off? To think so was not enough for Will. He must know.

One day Dick Hall complained of a bad toothache and stayed in his room. Will went to see him, sympathized most deeply, and recommended a first-rate dentist, but he had something more in his mind. Dick noticed the sparkle in his friend's eye and the little smile around his mouth, and the same thought occurred to him.

"Oh, no, you don't," he protested. "I know just what you're thinking. You want to inject some Mama Coca in my face. I don't want any experiments tried on me."

Will answered quietly but persistently. "It should be possible to deaden that pain so the dentist can fill your tooth easily."

"Look, Will," Dick said very positively, "I know the theory we've been working on, and I believe in it; but let's prove it on a dog or something, and not on me. Besides," he added rather triumphantly, "did you read what Wölfler says in the paper this morning?"

"I haven't seen the paper," Will replied patiently.

"Well, it's in the news from Germany," Dick continued.

"He says positively that cocaine injected in the tissues is use-less as an anesthetic."

Will was not one to give up. "I know he's a great surgeon, but I happen to think he's wrong. We've seen how the numb-ing effect follows the course of the nerve plexus. A numb nerve should not be able to carry pain. As for your tooth, we have seen this to be true of all accessible nerves except the inferior dental. Why shouldn't it be true there?"

"Sounds reasonable," Dick admitted, "but why pick on me? I've got troubles enough right now."

For a few minutes Will sat on the edge of the bed in silence. Then he spoke again in his quiet way. "I tell you what, Dick. If I let you inject a few minims in my dental nerve, will you go with me to the dentist and let me do it there?"

Dick smiled in spite of his pain. "You *are* persistent. All right. I'll agree."

Will had come prepared, and soon had a syringe filled with a drop or two of Mama Coca. Then he sat back in a chair and gave instructions in his usual calm, clinical man-ner.

"The injection must be made inside the mouth, and above the point where the nerve enters the tooth canal. This is important, as we have seen that the effect is downward and not upward. Pick a tooth you can reach easily."

He handed the syringe to Dick, put his head back, and opened his mouth. Here was the true experimental scientist, putting himself on the operating table.

Dick skillfully inserted the needle of the syringe and forced the cocaine into the nerve of the tooth. He withdrew it and waited. Will closed his mouth and ground his jaws together.

"So far, so good," he said. "Now take this pocket knife and pound on the tooth."

Dick struck the tooth, gently at first and then harder. There was no sign of a wince from Will.

"Now," Will continued, "sterilize a needle, and push it into the gum."

Dick hesitated, but saw at once that Will was in earnest. The needle went in, a little at first and then a good half inch. Dick withdrew it.

Will spread out his hands in a questioning manner. "Does that convince you?" he asked.

Dick had to admit that it was a pretty conclusive demonstration and, true to his word, he went with Will to have his tooth attended to.

The dentist was a friend of Will, and he readily agreed to try the cocaine injection. The syringe was filled and about eight drops were injected into the nerve of Dick's tooth. Half an hour later the dentist put down his instruments. He had scraped very close to the nerve, and had filled the cavity. He couldn't believe that his patient had felt no pain. It was a novel experience for him. For Will and Dick, it was a triumphant moment. They were well on their way toward proving that this new drug could destroy sensation and hence pain, not only when put on the surface, but when injected into and beneath the skin, thus blocking, or shutting off, part of the nerve. Will even found that the amount of cocaine mixed with water could be reduced to a minute quantity and still produce anesthesia if injected into the nerve plexus. An editorial appeared in the New York *Medical Journal* describing the experiments of Halsted and Hall, and Will published a letter in the same *Journal* explaining the value of deep injections of a very weak solution of cocaine and water.

Chapter

14

THE SUCCESS OF THIS FIRST EXPERIMENT WITH COCAINE IN-jection led Will Halsted to try its effect in a variety of surgical operations. He had earned a considerable degree of independence in his hospitals, and his methods were not questioned by those in authority. He was master in his own clinics. He removed a small cystic tumor from one patient, amputated the leg of another, and removed a tooth nerve from a woman suffering with severe neuralgia. All these operations were done without any suffering on the part of the patient. Operation followed operation. It was a glorious new field, and Will's enthusiasm knew no bounds. He seemed to have conquered pain, and he began to experiment on himself. The reported effect of Mama Coca on the Peruvian Indians proved to be quite true. Whether the leaf was chewed, snuffed up the nose, or taken into the system by injection, the result was the same—a feeling of complete tirelessness. Sleep seemed unnecessary; the mind was un-usually clear. Will and his colleagues were able to work long hours without rest. It was magic to Will. Always a hard worker, he was overjoyed at this gift of new strength.

Then the blow fell. It all began during a routine operation. The patient was on the table; all preparations were made;

everyone was in his or her place. Will held out his hand for the scalpel, and brought it into position for the first incision. He hesitated, drew back a moment, rubbed his eyes with the back of his hand, and leaned over again. His eyes had not deceived him. His hand and the razor-sharp scalpel were trembling. If he saw it, he knew that a dozen other pairs of eyes had seen it also. His usual deft, mathematical incision would be impossible. A vision of Dr. Borridine with his knife poised flashed into his mind. The same decision must be made here, only this time he was his own accuser. He straightened up, handed the scalpel back, motioned to his assistant to continue the operation, and walked none too steadily from the room.

He refused a cab whose eager driver pulled up to the curb. He wanted fresh air, and he breathed deeply as he walked home. It made him feel a little better physically, but he still had the terrible feeling of depression that had begun when he looked down and saw his hands trembling. The hands he had always been so proud of—those solid, capable hands that had saved so many lives—had betrayed him like a pair of false, faithless friends.

At home he sat down in a chair by the window. There was so much to be done. He had been feeling so tireless and eager, and now all of a sudden he didn't seem to care. He took a sniff of powdered cocaine. He and Dick often tried this at the theater if the show was boring. The powdered residue ticked his nostrils, but almost instantly he felt better. Good old Mama Coca. She had the answer. He would be all right the next morning. He must just have been too tired. He held his hand up at arm's length. There was no sign of trembling, and his confidence came back.

A few hours later Dick Hall came by. He seemed worried, and sat silent for a minute or two. Finally he said quietly, "I was in the operating room this afternoon, Will."

"That was probably foolish of me," Will replied casually. "I guess I was just overtired."

Dick shook his head. "Not you, Will. I've known you a long time, and I have yet to see you overtired. At least I've never seen you show it. That's what worried me."

There was a tone of genuine seriousness in his friend's voice, and Will was puzzled. "I don't quite understand, Dick," he said. "I'm not sick. I've been resting, and I feel much better."

"I don't altogether understand it, either," Dick replied, "but I have an idea. When you came into the operating room this afternoon, I had a feeling that something was wrong. I've known you pretty well, and I would be apt to notice any change."

Will remembered, now that Dick brought it up, that he had had a rather strange feeling when he entered the operating room. It never occurred to him that it was apparent to anyone but himself, and at the time he had thought little of it. "And you did notice a change?" he asked.

"Yes," Dick said rather hesitantly. "I didn't think too much about it at the time; but when your hands trembled and you left the room, I remembered it. You were perspiring, something I have never seen you do at an operating table."

"What are you driving at?"

"There was an expression on your face I had never seen before—a sort of stare, and you walked a little as though you were picking your way over a rough path."

"That could be fatigue," Will repeated. He was beginning to see that it might be something else, perhaps some real sickness; but he persisted in denying it. "Look at me now. I'm rested, and I'm better."

Dick put his hand on Will's arm. "Tell me," he said. "When you came home, did you lie down? Did you eat anything or take any medicine? Just what did you do?"

"No, I didn't lie down," Will replied. "Let me see. I had a drink of water, and sat over there by the window in that easy chair. I felt I needed rest. I took a pinch of cocaine, and read a book. Then you came in."

"Mama Coca," Dick murmured, nodding his head.

Will straightened up. He hadn't thought of this and it opened a terrifying prospect. "You mean—you think that the cocaine had something to do with it?"

Dick did not answer at once, and then not directly. "Have you read a book by Thomas DeQuincy called *Confessions of an English Opium Eater?*"

"Yes, but that was opium." Will couldn't bring himself to believe what Dick was implying.

"True," continued Dick, "but remember that opium is derived from a plant just as cocaine is, and it happens that we know something about opium. I spoke, just now, of your expression as you came into the operating room. When I saw your hands trembling, the thought suddenly occurred to me. Being a doctor, I suppose I made a quick diagnosis. I saw two symptoms of some drug, and the only drug we have been using in any quantity is cocaine. What else could I think? You tell me that you took some cocaine this afternoon by snuffing, and felt better at once. Do you follow me?"

Will understood only too well. His enthusiasm and the success of his operations had made him overlook a possibility that Dick Hall saw much more objectively. The two doctors sat silently in thought, and their thoughts were much the same. If this unknown drug with which they had been experimenting was even half as dangerous as opium, Will Halsted might be only the first victim. Six men had used it in varying doses.

Will argued that the Indians had used it constantly with no ill effect. Dick reminded him that there were no records of diseases or deaths among the primitive Indians, so there was no way of being sure. They discussed it for more than an hour, and finally decided to give up all use of it for the time being—as an experiment—and to advise the other four to do the same. What the results would be they didn't know, but there seemed no other course open to them.

A week went by. Will had turned his surgical work over to another man, and limited himself to work in the laboratory. He was afraid of what might happen.

One day, about the middle of the following week, a great feeling of depression returned to him—a feeling of complete indifference to his work. His dreams and the whole world of reality seemed to be collapsing around him. Visions of all the wonderful things he would do in surgery suddenly became dim and unimportant. Instead of working far into the night with eager enthusiasm as he had been doing, he found himself tossing restlessly on his bed and looking into an empty future.

The next morning was no better. Sitting still was torture; and yet, when he got up, he couldn't seem to decide what he should do next, or where he should go. The day wore on. He paced the room. He even went as far as the third floor for no particular reason. He returned to his study with some sudden determination to do something; but when he reached his door, he couldn't seem to remember what he had planned to do. He knew where help was to be found. It was in a little phial behind a dainty Dresden shepherdess on the mantelpiece in the parlor. He called it Mama Coca, and it would bring him relief. Perhaps if he took just a little of it, he would have the strength to straighten himself out and get something done. He had an agreement with Dick Hall and the others, but he could break that. What did anything matter any more?

He started for the door to go downstairs to the parlor. Halfway down the stairs he heard the front doorbell. Reaching the ground floor, he glanced into the parlor. There was the little shepherdess guarding the phial of Mama Coca. The doorbell rang again. He crossed to the mantel. It would only take a minute, and then he could see who his visitor was. As he got to the mantelpiece he heard a key turn in the lock, and the door open. He paused, trying to think who had a key to his house. Then he heard Sam Vander Poel's voice. "William." He drew his hand back from the little shepherdess and turned to face Sam, standing in the door of the parlor. Somehow he sensed that this was not just a friendly visit.

"What is it, Sam?" he asked irritably.

Sam tossed his hat on a chair and stepped into the room. "I have just come from Dr. Welch. He's very worried about you. We talked about you for a long time." Sam's voice was very quiet and earnest.

"Oh?" was all that Will could manage in reply.

"He told me of the incident in the operating room last week. Being up in Albany, I hadn't heard anything about it. Dr. Welch thinks it could be very serious. As you know, he has followed your experiments with cocaine with great interest. From the start he had a feeling that you were treading on dangerous ground but, knowing your success in other experiments, he said nothing. Now he wishes he had. He thinks that your illness is due to the cocaine you have been using. I agree with him."

"Dick Hall and I reached that same conclusion," Will put in abruptly. "We advised the rest not to use it for a while. A few weeks should prove it one way or the other. As a matter of fact, the supply is just about exhausted; so we must wait awhile anyway."

"And until you get a new supply, what do you propose doing?" Sam asked.

"I don't follow you," Will answered.

"I think I can make it quite clear," Sam continued. "Just a moment ago I saw you try to take some cigarette papers from your pocket. You gave it up because your hand was trembling. Right now you are perspiring. You're an unusually healthy man, William, and these symptoms are most unusual for you. Don't you realize that it isn't the drug alone that is doing this to you? It is the fact that you haven't any drug that is dangerous. You've become dependent on it."

"I know I'm nervous just now," Will admitted, "but if I keep off the drug I'm sure I'll feel better." Even as he said this he felt vaguely that he was wrong, but he didn't seem to have the will to admit it. "At least there is no proof that I won't," he continued.

"I wish I were sure of that, but I'm afraid you're wrong. Addiction to a drug is not a pleasant thing to realize. You mustn't let the success of a few experiments with it as an anesthetic blind you to the other side of the picture." Sam paused. "Dr. Welch wants you to go away from here for a while," he went on. "There is a hospital in Providence, run by a Dr. Sawyer, and—"

"That's ridiculous," Will interrupted, and there was a little anger in his voice at being told something he didn't want to believe. "A week is no test. I'll probably be all right in a few days. I took more than the others because it was my idea. It naturally hit me the hardest. I'm the only one who has been hurt."

"I'm afraid not," Sam replied, and there was a tone of finality in his voice that made Will turn suddenly to him.

"What makes you say that?"

The short silence was like the second before an execution.

"Because you are not the only one who has been hurt," he answered. "Jim Hartman, who was working with you, died last night—and it was not a pleasant death."

Suddenly the world of reality drew Will back from his mood of depression, only to make the depression deeper. It was like a nightmare that didn't end with an awakening.

Chapter
15

A FEW DAYS LATER WILL SAT IN THE OFFICE OF DR. WELCH in Bellevue Hospital. Here, he thought to himself, he had sat a few short years ago, a confident, successful young surgeon with great ideas. He had even done battle with the trustees of Bellevue in order to get a tent to help him carry out these ideas. Now, as he sat by Dr. Welch's desk, he was a patient seeking help—a sick man whose illness, unless cured, might mean the end of all his hopes.

"Will," Dr. Welch was saying, "four years ago you saved your sister's life by doing something that had never before been tried, and a year later you saved the life of your mother under much the same conditions. That took courage." He paused as though to emphasize his next thought. "Right now I am asking you to save your own life. I'll help you all I can, but it is going to take even more of that same sort of courage on your part. Sam and I have a plan. Will you do as I say?"

"Why should you take *any* trouble for me?" Will asked.

The fact that Welch and Vander Poel were personally very fond of Will went without saying, so Dr. Welch answered with a different reason. "Let's put it this way. I am a doctor, and I selfishly want to prevent my profession from losing a man with your originality and skill. We need what you alone can give to surgery. Does that answer your question?"

Will looked at Welch rather nonplussed. He had never thought of himself as indispensable to anyone. He had done his work because he loved it, and it had become his life. For a moment he couldn't reply, and Welch went on. "I have an idea, Will, about this new drug. We actually know little about it, but the chances are that it acts much as opium does. It forces us—you in particular—to face a challenge. It undoubtedly acts on the brain as soon as the system becomes saturated with it. It works against one's will power. The challenge is to prove that your will, or the will of anyone struck by the drug, is stronger than the drug itself. So it is not just you, as valuable as you are. You are in a position to prove to other men and women who may fall victims that the habit can be overcome. Will you accept the challenge?"

Welch knew Will very well, and felt sure of the answer to such a direct question. He was not disappointed.

"What do you want me to do?" Will asked quietly.

"In the first place you must give up all your work—resign from all your hospitals and give up any private practice. What you have to do will take every bit of your thought and energy. It will need the strength and courage that can come only from you." He went on to explain that with Sam Vander Poel's help he had secured a small schooner and three capable sailors. As soon as possible she would sail for the Windward Islands with Will and himself as passengers.

Sam had originally mentioned the Butler Hospital in Providence, and the idea had been distasteful to Will. This change was undoubtedly due to Dr. Welch. He protested again, however, that he could not impose so much on his friend. Dr. Welch insisted that they both needed a rest, they were both fond of the sea, and a few weeks away from the atmosphere of a hospital would be good for both of them. Will gave in. The day was set, and in less than a week Will stepped aboard the *Bristol* in New York Harbor.

Her rather beamy hull was painted more for preservation than for looks. Her decks and fittings were clean if not polished. Fore- and aft-rigged, she was clearly built for seaworthiness rather than for beauty. Dr. Welch and Will had two small cabins aft. The three sailors, known simply as the Captain, Al, and Joe, bunked forward. They were old salts and asked no questions. Headed on a course to the southeast, the little ship soon left the mainland behind. The sailors knew their job well and got everything possible from the *Bristol*. Will chatted with them, watched them at work, and occasionally eased a sheet or leaned on a halyard. At these times he felt happy and hopeful. There were, though, hours of unspeakable agony filled with delirious visions and moods of dark depression, ended only by a small dose of cocaine. Will never took any without Dr. Welch's consent, and he tried desperately to lengthen the periods between doses. It was a constant, humiliating, persistent fight.

Four days out, running close-hauled on a brisk southwest breeze, the *Bristol* was well on its way to the Caribbean. Will was sitting by the windward rail. He was not in good shape. He had stretched his luck further than at any other time since they had sailed. He felt hot, sick, and nervous. The sea was rough, and the wind gusty. He would go below to Dr. Welch and get some relief. He started to rise. He heard the helmsman shout; saw the main boom swing crazily out to port, the broken ends of the sheet dragging in the water. The sailor brought the *Bristol's* head up into the wind, and the heavy boom swung back. It caught the man on the side of his head and flung him sprawling at Will's feet. The Captain seized the wheel and steadied the ship. Will looked down. The man on the deck was bleeding badly from his head, but

Will just looked at him. Movement seemed impossible. Or was it that he didn't care? He knew perfectly well that he should stop the bleeding. He knew where the first-aid kit was kept. It was a routine job; but he just stood and looked, incapable of acting. Dr. Welch, roused from a nap by the helmsman's shout, appeared at the hatchway. Taking in the situation, he acted promptly and the injured man was soon lying comfortably on his bunk.

Will slipped below. Instinctively he reached for the little phial—and lay back on his bunk, suddenly relaxed. His body was tired from the strain of the last few hours, and his eyes closed drowsily. Half an hour later he opened them to see Dr. Welch sitting on the edge of his bunk. Will's mind was clear now. The realization that he, a doctor, had done nothing to help an injured man came to him with the shock of real pain. He rose on his elbow and started to speak, whether to justify himself or to apologize he didn't know. Dr. Welch interrupted him.

"Poor Joe got a nasty crack on the head. The sheet, being hauled in close, got snarled in the pulley, and a sudden gust was too much for it. Joe was afraid of a jibe and pulled the boat into the wind. The natural thing happened. The boom swung back. He's all right now though."

Will swung his legs onto the floor. "I was there when it happened," he began, "and I—"

Dr. Welch put his hand on his shoulder. He spoke kindly. "What happened out there was out of your hands, Will. Remember I told you that this cocaine gets into the brain. It numbs your decent thoughts. It's powerful. What you did, or didn't do, was not a fault, but it should help to show you what you are up against. You've just got to make up your mind to be more powerful than the drug. Now try to get a little more sleep. I'll go on deck and see if I can do some sailoring." Halfway up he leaned down from the hatchway and said, "Remember, Will, your job is the future—not the past."

The rough weather of the Atlantic gave all hands plenty to do, and Will found that, during these periods of hard physical work, he was able to go much longer without the cocaine. Just before they left the Atlantic, a school of flying fish was sighted—beautiful, sparkling creatures six or seven inches long. They looked like little shining bits of blue steel as they wriggled in the nets. They were excellent eating and the crew did justice to them. The Captain claimed that they really flew like birds, pointing out the large fins, like wings, that stretched back as far as the tail. Will was doubtful. With the care he would have used in a demonstration to a class of young surgeons, he laid open one of the little fish with his pocketknife. In his best clinical manner he traced the fin muscles, and pointed out how small they were compared with the heavy muscles that moved the tail. It was obvious, he said to his strangely assorted class in anatomy, that the little fish used his tail to leap from the water when attacked by an enemy, and that the long fins served merely as means of gliding. The crew were impressed if not convinced. Dr. Welch smiled. To him, the demonstration meant more than a proof of any theory about flying fish. He saw that Will had lost none of his skill or enthusiasm.

Beyond the doldrums the little schooner had to beat against the steady, easterly trade winds. It was slow going, and the monotony of the days worked on Will's nerves. He slipped back many times to his reliance on the little doses of cocaine permitted him. He was continually grateful that Dr. Welch never rebuked him, scarcely ever referred to it. Instead he talked of incidents of the trip and the problem of medicine in these remote islands.

"When we get home," he said one day, "I want you to

come down to Baltimore and stay with me. You'll be interested in the plans for the new hospital to be connected with Johns Hopkins University. It's tremendous. The biggest thing yet in medicine. I'm proud to say that they have given me the chair of pathology. Dr. Billings, who is really responsible for the whole thing, is a very old friend of mine." He paused. "I tell you all this, Will, because—well, there might be a place for you there sometime."

Will demurred. He had his own work in New York, if he was ever to have any work again. Deep in his heart he wondered, but he kept his thoughts to himself. "Your job is the future," Dr. Welch had said, and Will knew there was no room for discouraging thoughts.

Then early one morning they made their first landfall. Two conical mountains rose majestically through the white mist.

"The Pitous on Santa Lucia," the Captain told them, and soon they were in the lee of the British-owned island. The red-roofed houses of the little town lay along the edge of the blue water, some of them straggling up through bright green spots of cane fields to the tree-covered hills and mountains.

Their plans allowed for five days on land before their return trip. The ship had to be stocked, and there were minor repairs to be made. The two doctors spent their time ashore. When Will had first seen the little town from the sea, he had thought it beautiful. As he left the dock and the only large street of the town closed around him, his spirits fell. Rain and sun washed and brightened the roofs, but where there was no sun, and where the rain could not reach, there was darkness and dirt. They found the English doctor, a discouraged little man named Lewis, who was only too glad to talk to strangers. Yes, he admitted, the town was not clean, and there were many deaths from *yaws*—a word, he explained, used for almost any disease caused by dirty conditions. There had been a hospital; but in 1884 it had burned to the ground and, so far, the plans for a new one had not been completed. He was using his own house for the few cases that needed constant treatment, but he had no one to help him except two native women who were of practically no use.

One look around the room used as a ward convinced Will that no one there had ever heard of Lister or Koch. There was only one patient, lying on one of the half-dozen mattresses. He was a little boy of about fourteen who, Lewis explained, must have eaten some sort of poisoned root, and had a constant stomach ache. Will asked the doctor what he was doing for the boy, and Lewis gave a gesture of despair. "What can we do? Purgatives, quinine. We must clear the poison out, you know." He spoke in a confidential, professional way as one doctor to another; but Will sensed a sort of defensive attitude, as though Lewis were not sure at all. The little patient was sobbing, and Will, with a polite "May I?" to Lewis, knelt beside the mattress on which the boy was lying. He turned down the thin blanket, and deftly ran his fingers over the boy's abdomen. Then he put back the blanket and stood up.

"Do you have any surgical instruments, Doctor?" he asked.

"Oh, yes," Lewis replied in a rather offhand way, "but I seldom use them except to cut out the poison of a snake. We have a very venomous kind on the island, you know. It's known as a fer-de-lance and—"

Will cut his ramblings short. "You should use them on this boy." His voice had a commanding tone that he hadn't used for weeks. The sight of the suffering child seemed for the moment to have cleared up the cloud of depression that had been with him so much during the last few weeks.

"What makes you say that?" Lewis asked.

"There is no doubt in my mind," Will replied, "that he has an infected appendix."

"That's nonsense. The boy has a stomach ache, and as soon as he has been cleaned out he'll be all right." Lewis' voice was irritable and defensive.

"How long has he been here?" Will asked.

"About a week," was the short reply.

"You mean to tell me, Dr. Lewis," Will said in an astonished voice, "that after a week of purgatives and quinine this child still has a stomach ache?"

Lewis was clearly angry. "Are you questioning my diagnosis?" he asked sharply.

Dr. Welch was about to intervene, but Will gave him no chance. "We can all make mistakes, Doctor. This child will die of peritonitis if the appendix is not removed at once. In fact, if it has perforated it may be too late already."

The momentary silence was broken only by the sobbing of the little figure, now curled up in pain on the mattress. "But I've never done such an operation," Lewis protested. "It is frowned upon by most doctors."

Will's reply was curt and confident. "Not by American doctors. I have seen it done and I have done it myself. With your permission and help I should like to do it now."

Little Doctor Lewis had his pride. He had already protested against the seeming interference of the American doctor. He was alone on the island; he was discouraged, and in his weary eyes the little boy was just another native.

"I have no anesthetic except whisky," he said.

Will caught Welch's eye. They were both thinking the same thing. Welch shook his head, but Will ignored the gesture and turned back to Lewis.

"I am prepared to supply the anesthetic, Doctor, in return for the use of your instruments. Will you go along with me?"

Lewis shrugged his shoulders, went to a bureau, and took out a leather case. "You'll find them in good order," he said as he handed the case to Will. "As I said, I've hardly used them; and they have not been exposed to dampness."

Will checked the instruments. He was master of the situation now. His orders were confident. "I must go to the schooner to get the anesthetic. Sterilize these instruments in boiling water and whisky. Have the boy ready on the table with as many sterile dressings as you can dig up, and plenty of boiling water and soap. Have you any catgut or silk—or anything for suturing?"

"Much of it was lost in the fire," Lewis answered, "but I'll look around."

"If you can't find any, get some hair from a horse's tail or mane. Sterilize it and have it ready. I'll be back in half an hour."

Dr. Welch followed Will out of the house. "Will," he protested, "you can't do this. You have barely enough cocaine for yourself and—let me see your hands." Will held out his hands. Welch leaned over them. Then he looked at Will. "Do you expect to operate with hands that shake? You'd do better to let the boy die naturally." There was a trace of sarcasm in his voice.

"I'll take an extra shot myself. I'll be steady enough to operate," Will answered confidently.

"And after that?" Welch asked, thinking of the depleted supply.

"We'll talk about that later. First things first," Will replied. "You go back and see that that fool doctor doesn't do anything too stupid. I'll get Cap to take me out to the schooner."

He turned and was off. In half an hour he was back with the three sailors in tow.

In the lazy little town anything unusual was quickly noticed, and a crowd of curious natives had gathered around the doctor's house. Will immediately assigned Al and Joe to act as guards to keep everyone at a distance, and he took the Captain into the house with him.

Thanks to Dr. Welch's prodding, Dr. Lewis had been able to find more material than he had thought he had. He even found a spool of catgut. The child was already on a table, sobbing pitifully, while Dr. Welch washed him carefully. Will scrubbed his own hands as best he could, filled the syringe with a solution of cocaine and boiled water, and leaned over the prostrate little figure. As the injection began to take effect, the muscles relaxed. The child was given a solution of whisky and water to quiet him, and Will made the first incision. Dr. Lewis held the child's feet to prevent any involuntary movement. The Captain rather enthusiastically held his hands, keeping up a steady stream of fatherly if slightly salty talk in the boy's ear. Dr. Welch acted as assistant. Will soon had the appendix exposed, a long, useless sac attached to the intestine. It was badly inflamed, and obviously full of poisonous liquid. Will skillfully tied it off, and then cut it away from the intestine. He worked fast. The condition of the appendix demanded it and, besides, he never had any sure way of knowing just how long his own dose of cocaine would keep his mind clear and his hands steady. He deftly cleaned out and sutured the wound, covered the child with a blanket, and turned to Dr. Lewis.

"We got to it in time, Doctor. It was not perforated, so there should be no intestinal infection. But no purgatives. Keep the child quiet. I'll be in every day to see him until we leave."

He used the word "we" in referring to the operation, and

spoke as one consulting doctor to another, because he didn't want to offend, and Dr. Lewis, impressed by Will's skill, showed his appreciation by complete cooperation.

They lengthened their stay to a week, and by that time the boy was well on his way to complete recovery. The native population was treating Will as some sort of magician. Will saw to it that any reference to what he had done included Dr. Lewis, so that, when they finally sailed, some of Will's glamour still clung to the discouraged little colonial doctor.

Will stepped aboard the *Bristol* for the homeward trip with a great feeling of uncertainty. The operation had reduced his supply of cocaine. He needed it less than he had coming out—of that he was pretty sure—and the thought gave him confidence. On the other hand, the knowledge that it was there if he really needed it had much to do with giving him strength to do without it. Ten days at sea with a reduced supply was a prospect he found hard to face. There was, though, no alternative, and he comforted himself with the thought that this might be his supreme test.

One thing gave him further confidence. After the accident on the trip out he had felt that the Captain had been disgusted with him for neglecting the injured sailor, and had lost respect for him. The appendix operation seemed to have changed all that. The Captain remarked on it at every opportunity. "I wouldn't have believed it if I hadn't seen it," or "The best stitching job I ever seen." He urged Will to help when the weather got a little rough, and appeared to enjoy having him around. The two became good friends.

The easterly trade winds made their going a little easier and, with only one or two rough days, they soon found themselves a few hundred miles off the Florida coast. Here the winds were southwesterly; but the *Bristol* trimmed well, and ran close enough to make good progress without too much beating. A few days before sighting land, Will began to feel the effects of his reduction in cocaine. He had done pretty well; but the strain was telling on him, and signs of the old depression were coming to him. For two days and nights he was delirious and seemed to recognize no one. The third day he became calmer, though he was still tired and haggard. Opening his eyes one morning, he met the gaze of the Captain sitting by his bunk. "You've had it kinda tough lately, matey," he said sympathetically, "but just keep your head into the wind and don't fall off too much, and you'll find a lee shore before you know it." Will smiled in spite of his feelings. He had never heard his troubles put just that way, and he liked it. Sitting in the sun on the deck, he repeated it to Dr. Welch the next day. The coast line of the Carolinas was in sight, and home port not too far away.

"I couldn't have put it better myself," Dr. Welch commented, "if I'd quoted all the philosophers from Plato to your friend William James. You're bucking the wind, Will. Just don't let it beat you off your course."

A day or so later they tied up at the dock in New York. Will said good-by to the Captain with genuine regret. The man had given him a new strength, and he was more than grateful. Dr. Welch insisted that Will go to the hospital in Providence. He would like Dr. Sawyer, he said, and a few weeks of concentrated medical care was what he needed.

"And after that?" Will asked. He was thinking of Dr. Welch's offer of work with him in Baltimore.

The answer was reassuring. "Why, join me in Baltimore of course." It was a load off Will's mind.

The weeks he spent at Butler Hospital in Providence were most successful. He found Dr. Sawyer a much older man than Dr. Welch but just as warm a friend. The treatment was much less violent than what he had become used to on his sea trip. A milder drug was substituted for the cocaine, the food was nourishing, and his many friendly talks with Dr. Sawyer on general as well as on professional subjects gave him a feeling of being again an essential part of the world of medicine. His stay was saddened by the unexpected death of Dr. Sawyer. Will sat by his bedside for long hours before he died, and on his last visit the older man urged Will not to be discouraged.

"I've seen enough of drugs," he said quietly, "to know that it is not an easy thing to break off. Many more fail than succeed. In your case you are, at this moment, succeeding. Don't let anything stop you from trying. You are young—is it thirty-four? Our profession needs you. Think of it that way and don't let modesty interfere."

These friendly words, combined with those of Dr. Welch and the Captain, bolstered Will's determination. Only a few weeks after Dr. Sawyer's death he was considered sufficiently in control of himself to leave the hospital.

Dr. Welch was as good as his word. He had arranged for quarters in Baltimore, and the use of his laboratory, and Will soon felt completely at home. The work in the laboratory filled his days. Men whom Will had known personally or by reputation were working together on various phases of experimental pathology—such men as Walter Reed, studying bacteriology, and Abraham Flexner, working on the problems connected with epidemic diseases and poisons. Each in his own field was investigating the basic changes brought about by diseases in the human body, and in this way getting closer to possible cures and preventatives.

Will's interest was surgery, as it always had been, and the two years he spent with Dr. Welch gave him the chance he had never before had to perfect his knowledge of anatomy. He worked on the bodies of men and women who had died of cancer, and whose relatives had given the authorities permission to perform autopsies in the hope of finding some cure for this fatal disease. Meticulously Will studied the effect of the malignant tumor on nerves, muscles, blood, and the various organs of the body. To find the infection, to figure out a way to prevent its spread, and to devise an operation that would prolong a stricken person's life became his daily task. As yet he performed no operations himself; but he watched others, noting carefully and critically every move they made, and formulating in his mind ways of avoiding their failures. He made a careful study of the anatomy of the wall of the intestine, and discovered that the strength of the wall to hold a suture lay in the submucous coat. The many failures in intestinal operations were largely due to ignorance of this fact, resulting in faulty suturing. Will showed that the stitch, to be properly taken, must engage this submucous coat.

His own troubles were almost completely forgotten, and only very occasionally, at greater and greater intervals, did he have to fight any desire for the drug that had taken three years out of his life.

One day early in 1889 he and Dr. Welch were walking through the buildings of the almost completed hospital given by Johns Hopkins to the university. They had often discussed it. It was to be, as Dr. Welch had told Will, the greatest contribution to medicine ever made. It was to serve all the sick, regardless of race, creed, or color. There were to be clinics for those unable to pay, and it was to be staffed by the top men in the various branches of the profession.

"As you know, Will," Dr. Welch was saying, "I am a trustee, and as such I share the responsibility of getting only the best men. The chair of surgery is still open. I have said nothing to Billings or any other of the trustees, but I want you."

This was said simply but in the rather positive way of a

man who, having thought something over for a long time, decides to come to the point. Simple as the words were, the depth of their meaning was not lost on Will. Not only did Dr. Welch want him in the vitally important position but he must also believe that the nightmare years of cocaine were over.

Will hesitated to tell himself that he was sure, although in his heart he knew they were. "But I—" he began.

Dr. Welch interrupted him at once. "I know just what you're going to say, Will. Don't think I haven't given this a lot of thought. Remember that, in a way, we've been through this thing together, and—"

This time, Will broke in. The moment called for plain speaking. "I appreciate your confidence. But what about the other trustees? They all know of my sickness. My breakdown at an operation in New York three years ago is no secret. I'm not so sure of the wisdom of it myself."

They had reached Dr. Welch's office in the laboratory, and were soon seated by his desk.

"I want you to do something for me before you decide, Will," Dr. Welch said. "Will you do it?"

"Of course," Will replied without hesitation. Dr. Welch opened a drawer and took out a small phial, one only too familiar to Will.

"I don't need to tell you what this is," Welch went on. "I want you to take it. I want you to keep it with you night and day for a month. It has a seal on it. I want you to return it to me with the seal unbroken."

"You mean if I can do this it will prove to the trustees that I am quite normal again?" Will said.

Welch hesitated. "Not exactly, Will. I don't believe I shall even mention it to them."

"Then I don't see how—" Will began, but was stopped by a gesture from Welch.

"The trustees will take my word in the matter," he went on. "An addict to drugs or alcohol is cured only when he has gained confidence in himself. This test is for you—not the trustees. Prove it to yourself, and I'll carry on from there. Personally, I think you have reached the lee shore that the Captain spoke about." He handed Will the phial. "Keep this with you and find out."

Chapter

16

THE LITTLE PHIAL BECAME A SYMBOL FOR WILL. HE COULDN'T help thinking of the ancient Greek legend of Pandora and her box. All the troubles of the world escaped because she took off the cover. If he could keep his bottle sealed for a month, the troubles that the cocaine represented would never escape. Pandora had let everything escape except hope. Will vowed that he would hold on to this. He kept the phial with him at all times. At night it was on the table beside his bed, and during the day in his waistcoat pocket. Every time he touched the unbroken seal his confidence grew. It was like a game with his future as the stake. Also like a game, the more he played it the easier it became and the more expert he became in playing it. Even before the month was over, he knew that he couldn't lose.

Five weeks had gone by when Will received an official call to the office of Dr. John S. Billings. The doctor had been librarian of the Surgeon General's office in Washington, and was now Chairman of the Board of Trustees of the Johns Hopkins Hospital. The two had met informally at a small dinner party shortly after Will had reached Baltimore in 1887, but both were busy men and had seen little of each other since.

"As you know," Dr. Billings began, "it is up to me to find the men for our staff here. I have heard reports of your

158

work in New York with much interest. You have skill and
imagination, Halsted. Dr. Welch has expressed the greatest
confidence in your future." He paused and looked questioningly at Will. Then he continued. "I understand that you
have given up your connections in New York, and are free
at the moment. Am I right?"

"That's right, Doctor," Will replied, trying to suppress the
eagerness he felt.

"I have discussed the matter carefully with the other
trustees," Billings went on. "We are prepared to offer you
the position of Chief of the Dispensary and Acting Surgeon
to the hospital. The appointment is to be for one year. Will
you accept it?"

Will's heart sank. A one year's appointment was not exactly what he had hoped for. There must still be some doubt
in the minds of the trustees, for this was obviously a term
of probation. Then Will's mind translated the word probation into a challenge. He quickly accepted it. When he left
the office a few minutes later, he was a member of the staff
of Johns Hopkins. For the next two months he not only
carried on his own experimental work in Welch's laboratory
but made and carried out plans for the Dispensary, or Out-
Patient Department, of the new hospital.

Then the great day of the opening came, May 7, 1889.
The city of Baltimore turned out in festive mood. Clearly,
as Dr. Welch had told Will years before, this project was to
be the greatest thing in medicine. Doctors, lawyers, politi-
cians, government officials, and foreign representatives
gathered on the grounds. Newspapers from all over the
world were represented. Even the day itself provided clear
blue skies and a warm summer breeze.

Will sat near the speakers' platform. Dr. King, the president of the university, made some introductory remarks,
and was followed by Dr. Billings. Much of what the chair-

man said was familiar to Will. He had watched the buildings grow; he had seen how carefully the rooms, wards, and laboratories had been planned. In his many talks with Dr. Welch he had learned of the unselfish ideals of Mr. Johns Hopkins. But as he listened, his enthusiasm and confidence were renewed. He was a part of this whole ambitious scheme. It never occurred to him that he had achieved something unique for so young a man. He was only thirty-seven.

". . . and another point insisted upon by Mr. Hopkins," he heard Dr. Billings say, "was that the hospital should form a part of the medical school of the university, and every opportunity should be given for higher medical education."

Especially this, thought Will as he listened. He was the only surgeon on the staff, and the instruction of young surgeons was his business. There must be no slip-up here. He thought back to Dr. Borridine; he thought of little Dr. Lewis, who used his surgical instruments only in cases of snakebite; he thought of all the surgeons who considered themselves brilliant because they worked with speed but who sewed up wounds over germs and decaying tissue, dooming their patients to death from infection. All this ignorance must be brought to an end.

His thoughts were interrupted by applause. Other speakers were announced. His friend Dr. Welch said a few words, and then Governor Jackson of Maryland formally declared the hospital open. More applause, a sudden burst of buzzing voices, and a scraping of chairs—and the ceremonies were over. Will chatted aimlessly with a few friends, and moved toward the exit with the crowd.

Over the chattering he heard his name called, and turned to see Dr. Welch beckoning to him. Pushing his way upstream, he was soon behind the crowd. Standing with Dr. Welch was a young woman whom Will had already noticed sitting with a group of nurses.

"This is Caroline Hampton, Will," Dr. Welch said. "She is a member of our staff—head nurse in Surgery. I don't believe you two have met." He turned to the tall, aristocratic-looking woman and bowed slightly. "Miss Hampton, may I present Dr. Halsted, our acting surgeon." Naturally shy, Will had developed a rather abrupt attitude when meeting people. It was as though he wanted to size them up before giving anything of himself. It was not rudeness; perhaps it was more like a careful doctor's hesitation about giving a hasty diagnosis. As Will bowed to acknowledge Dr. Welch's introduction, he suddenly realized that he felt completely sure of his diagnosis. He saw a warm smile, and a pair of eyes that seemed to expect friendliness. They were, moreover, the eyes of one who was accustomed to getting what she chose to expect.

"Of course I've known of Dr. Halsted for some time. I trained at the New York Hospital. You have many admirers there, Doctor."

The voice was gentle and honest. Will was quite used to having strangers compliment him. They generally wanted some favor, and Will had learned to disregard them. This was probably another reason why his manner often seemed abrupt. This time he felt instinctively that the remark was made without thought of any favor. Miss Hampton was clearly one who had no need of asking favors, and Will admired her for it. The three exchanged pleasantries, and Miss Hampton excused herself. Dr. Welch watched her until she was out of earshot. Then he turned to Will as they started for the door.

"A remarkable woman. The hospital is most fortunate to have found her. She has only one fault as far as I know."

The idea of any imperfection in Miss Hampton had not occurred to Will, and his reply was one of surprise. "Really? What could that be?"

"She has a mind of her own," Dr. Welch explained. "She comes of an old, very aristocratic South Carolina family, and she finds it rather difficult at times to take orders from our head nurse."

Will was a little puzzled. "I thought she was the head nurse in Surgery."

"True," Dr. Welch replied, "but we have a woman who is head of the Nurses' Training School and who has the final say in all departmental questions. It was Billings' idea."

The two men walked in silence for a few minutes. Then Will spoke.

"It seems to me that a woman of her apparent ability and character should be given pretty free rein. I don't know this other woman. But don't you think the hospital is, perhaps, making a mistake?"

"Frankly," Welch agreed, "I'm not too happy about it. The difficulty is that her appointment to Johns Hopkins, and that of the supervising nurse, is official as of today. Had I spoken when I first noticed the arrangement, something might have been done; but now I'm afraid it would be difficult to change the situation."

Will thought this over. "Couldn't she stay on the staff but be transferred to some other post?" he asked. Then he added, almost unthinkingly, "As a matter of fact, I could use her in my operating room. She would be responsible only to me."

Dr. Welch smiled slightly. "That might be a solution, Will. Let me speak to Billings."

Speaking to Billings was largely a matter of form. Dr. Welch's opinion on any subject connected with Johns Hopkins was almost invariably followed. Several days passed. Will waited impatiently for word from Dr. Billings, and found himself looking forward to seeing Miss Hampton again. Her calmness, her quiet, assured way of speaking

were traits that appealed to him. It occurred to him that in
earlier, more active days these would not have seemed so
attractive. He had felt this change in his nature ever since
the dark, tragic days of his cocaine experience. Was it, he
wondered, because he was older, or could it be that the
physical and emotional struggle against addiction had left
him with a desire only for quiet and study? Dr. Welch's faith
in him had carried him through the darkest part of his life.
His concern now was for the future, and somehow Caroline
Hampton became more and more a part of that future.

There was much routine work to be done and Will was
hardly out of his office. One day when he answered a knock
on the door, he was not too surprised to see Caroline Hampton. He started to speak, but she anticipated him.

"Dr. Welch said you wished to see me."

"Yes, Miss Hampton," he said in his best clinical manner.
"I should like to have a talk with you." He indicated a chair.
"Please sit down."

There was a dignity in the way she sat. Other young
nurses, and even some doctors, seemed to lose their self-
confidence in the presence of Dr. Halsted, but not Miss
Hampton. Rather, she was royalty granting an audience.

"Dr. Welch tells me that you have been transferred to my
operating room," Will began. There was a questioning tone
in the statement although he knew perfectly well that it
was he who had made the suggestion to Dr. Welch.

"Yes, Dr. Halsted."

Will studied the white file card on his desk. He had already read it twice. He knew that she had trained at Mt.
Sinai and New York hospitals, had worked in the operating
rooms and surgical wards, and because of her high ranking
had been assigned to the new hospital in Baltimore. He must
go over it again with her, though, just as he would with any
applicant for a position. He questioned her about the men

she had worked with, and the cases she had attended. Her
answers were always clear and concise. There was no attempt to impress him. Most young nurses had tried that sort
of thing. The more he questioned her the more sure he
became that he needed her a great deal more than she
needed him. Any ward or operating room in the hospital
would have a place for her. The problem seemed to be his
and not hers. He put the file card to one side.

"We have, as you probably know," he went on, "very
strict rules of asepsis in my operating room. In fact, they
have been considered so severe that many of my nurses in
New York and Bellevue Hospitals have refused to stay with
me."

A slight inclination of the head was her only acknowledg-
ment of this information. He went on to tell her what those
assisting at his operations had to do. He told her of the long
scrubbing with soap and water, the drenching with potas-
sium permanganate that turned the skin the color of a
"black eye" until it was brought back to normal flesh tone
through a third dose, this time of oxalic acid. Then, as if this
were not enough, his technique called for a fourth washing
with bichloride of mercury. All this was hard on the skin, he
reminded her. It often caused severe burning and itching
that was very painful. He paused.

"Does that seem unduly severe, Miss Hampton?"

She shook her head. "Not at all, Dr. Halsted. It's a question of a patient's life." This was said quietly and purely as a
matter of fact, in the manner of a dedicated nurse.

"I'm glad you see it that way, Miss Hampton. I think we
should get on very well together." He rose. "I shall expect
you Monday morning."

He closed the door quietly, sat down at his desk and
lighted a cigarette. It had all been very formal, as was
Will's habit in interviewing people. He always got down to

facts as quickly as possible. In this case he had known all the facts before he interviewed Miss Hampton. He had felt sure of her answers. He let one cigarette burn down, and lighted another from it. Smoking helped him think. He had often been asked why he didn't get married. His answer had always been that he hadn't had time, and he would get around to it later. Perhaps, he thought to himself as he watched the smoke rings, now at the age of thirty-eight he had at last reached that mysterious period which he had always referred to as "later."

Whatever the reason, as the weeks went by, he began to realize that his thoughts were constantly turning to Miss Hampton, or Caroline as he began thinking of her.

One day in the operating room Will noticed that she was suffering from a severe dermatitis of her arms and hands brought on by the irritating washing technique. It gave him deep concern. So much so, in fact, that he decided to do something about it. He had heard of an old-time German surgeon who used gloves. They were crude affairs, and in those dark days of surgery he had obviously done it to protect his own hands without thought of how the coarse gloves would irritate and infect the patient. Why not, Will thought, use gloves made of fine rubber which could be disinfected even more thoroughly than skin? In this way the patient would be protected as well as the surgeon and his assistants.

As usual when he had an idea Will went into action at once. He arranged with the Goodyear Rubber Company to make two pairs of gauntlet gloves of the very thinnest rubber. When they arrived they were the talk of the hospital. They helped Miss Hampton. This, of course, pleased Will, but he sensed something far more important. Covering the hands with thin rubber was revolutionary, and the hospital authorities recognized it. More rubber gloves were ordered.

Each assistant who handled the instruments was provided with a pair, and even the operating surgeon used them when making exploratory incisions into joints. Dr. Joseph C. Bloodgood, Will's house surgeon, claimed that the sense of touch was improved by the thin rubber, and he used them in a full-scale operation with great success. It was clear that rubber gloves had come to stay.

Will was not always in his operating room. His main responsibility, in his own eyes, was the group of young graduate surgeons who worked under him. They were hand-picked, and many applicants were turned down. They must be, Will determined, dedicated men. They had all had medical-school training. At Johns Hopkins, with Will Halsted as preceptor, they were permanent members of his staff, willing and eager to spend eight to ten years perfecting themselves in all techniques of surgery. This was Will's dream of years coming true.

In the early part of October, with five months of his probation, or challenge year as he preferred to think of it, behind him, Will was asked by Dr. Billings to give ward and operating-room privileges to a certain Dr. Hughes, a friend of his from California. This meant, of course, that the strange doctor would for a time replace one of the young members of his staff. The continuous, personal service that was Will's ideal would be broken into, and as a true experiment the system would fail. A refusal on his part might easily result in dismissal, but Will's mind was quickly made up. He politely explained to the California doctor the nature of the surgical service, and how it was impossible to grant Dr. Billings' request.

Was this, Will wondered, to be the end of his career at Hopkins? Dr. Billings had obviously expected him to grant his request. It would have been so easy, but Will's thoughts went back to what Sands had said about the experiment in asepsis: "There must be no loopholes." Will felt that he had acted in the only way possible, but he was not surprised when, a few days later, he received a message that Dr. Billings wanted to see him.

In his study Dr. Billings launched at once into his subject. "I'm sorry, Halsted, that you found it impossible for my friend Hughes to have service in surgery. He has quite a reputation on the West Coast. I'm sure you would have found him stimulating."

Will wished he wouldn't stretch the matter, and he merely agreed. "I'm sure of that, Dr. Billings."

"As a matter of fact," Dr. Billings went on, "Dr. Hughes found you very stimulating. I may add that that was the very word he used."

Will merely raised his eyebrows. He was waiting for the ax to fall. But the voice of doom went on in the same vein.

"I showed him over the hospital, especially the surgical wards and operating rooms. We discussed your theories of asepsis and wound healing, and I showed him your rubber gloves. He was most enthusiastic. In fact, he said he thought the time would come when even the operating surgeon would wear them. Before he left, he made a suggestion. Would you care to hear it?"

"Certainly," Will answered patiently.

"He said we should never let go of such a valuable man."

Will started to speak, but Billings cut him short. "Actually, Dr. Hughes' suggestion has been in the minds of the trustees for some time. Your present appointment was, I believe, for a year. I propose to cancel it. Would you accept a permanent position as Associate Professor of Surgery?"

Will had been waiting for the ax to fall. The preliminaries had taken place; the moment had arrived—and there was no ax. Instead, he was offered a future of unbelievable possibilities. It was as though the ax had actually fallen, and had cut him off from his immediate past. He tried to conceal his feelings of surprise as he accepted the position, and after a few routine arrangements he left Dr. Billings' office. There were two persons he went to at once with the news. One was Caroline Hampton, and he had some very special things to say to her. The other was Dr. Welch, whom he thanked over and over again for all his encouragement.

"I had nothing to do with this appointment," Welch protested.

"Perhaps not directly," Will agreed, "but you made it possible, and I am eternally grateful. There is, though, another favor I should like to ask of you, and I won't take No for an answer."

"Of course, Will—anything," Dr. Welch replied.

"My operating nurse, Miss Hampton, is resigning."

"Oh, I'm sorry for that," Dr. Welch said with surprise. "What reason does she give?"

"Well, I'm afraid it has to do with me," Will answered rather sadly.

Dr. Welch shook his head. "Same old story, eh? I think, Will, that you carry this strict asepsis a little too far. You say yourself that other nurses have walked out on you."

"Oh, but she isn't walking out on me," Will protested.

Dr. Welch was puzzled. "But I don't quite understand. You said she was resigning."

Will was thoroughly enjoying himself. "It's all very simple," he said with a twinkle. "Miss Hampton—Caroline and I are planning to be married. We want you to be our best man."

Dr. Welch was delighted, and congratulated Will most warmly. "You've picked a remarkable girl for your wife," he said.

"That's just it," Will replied. "Perhaps she's too remarkable. Sometimes I wonder what she sees in me."

Dr. Welch laughed, and slapped Will on the back. "That," he said, "is quite the proper attitude for a husband."

The engagement was short—only a few weeks. Dr. William Osler, Professor of Medicine at Johns Hopkins, gave a large dinner party in their honor, and many of Will's associates and students were present, including, of course, Dr. Welch. The wedding on June 4, 1890, in the little church at Columbia, South Carolina, was a simple ceremony. Their vows were exchanged, the minister gave them his blessing, and Caroline and Will walked down the aisle into the future.

Chapter

17

Both Caroline and Will had very definite ideas as to what that future was to be. They had talked it over from every angle during the few short weeks of their engagement, and they had sealed their decision irrevocably during their honeymoon at High Hampton, the family home in the Carolina mountains. Caroline would give up her profession entirely. William, as she chose to call him, had ambition enough for both of them, she told her friends; her work was to make it possible for him to realize it.

Baltimore and his work, in the winter, and the mountains of South Carolina, in the summer, became Will's routine. In the mountains he enjoyed the life of a country gentleman, raising dahlias; walking through the woods with his dogs; and even riding horseback so as not to be outdone by Caroline, who was an expert horsewoman. Being a Northerner born and bred, he found it a little hard at first to accustom himself to Southern ways. For a time he kept aloof from the native people. One day a completely unexpected incident changed this habit. It all had to do with a sick horse.

Out walking, Will had come upon a tourist stranded because one of his horses had developed a strange stiffness and moved only with the greatest difficulty. Will diagnosed the case as rheumatic fever. With Caroline's help he nursed the

CANCER, COCAINE AND COURAGE

animal back to strength. The stranger's gratitude might
have been the last word in the matter had not a farmer and
his wife watched the whole proceeding and told all their
friends about it. They all reasoned quite naturally that, if
he could cure a horse, Doc Halsted should be able to do
pretty well for a sick cow, or a dog, or even a chicken. One
thing led to another until it was no longer possible for Will
to stay aloof from the natives and, as "Doc," he gave advice
and help whenever it was asked.

He became almost a part of the landscape, moving along
remote country roads on some errand of mercy, walking
with a deliberate tread, his powerful shoulders slightly
stooped. He didn't always recognize each of his many new
friends, as he was very near-sighted; but he never failed to
give them a cheery greeting. Walking one day across the
fields and through the woods around High Hampton, he
dropped in at a mountaineer's cabin to inquire after a dog
whose leg he had set. He was met at the door by the man's
wife. Yes, the dog was doing fine; but Alexander, her husband, had got himself shot in the shoulder and couldn't get
out of bed. Would "Doc" look at him? "Doc" certainly
would and, with a friendly smile, he sat down on the edge
of the bed.

Will leaned over and began palpating the shoulder. Between the jaw and the shoulder blade there was a considerable lump, more than an inch high, and it needed only
a few minutes for Will's diagnosis. The bullet had injured
the artery of the neck region, and a tumor, or aneurysm, had
formed. Will explained the trouble in the simplest way he
could; gave a few instructions to Alexander's wife; and left,
promising to return the next day.

That night he explained to Caroline, in words he had been
unable to use to the old Negro and his wife, just how serious
Alexander's condition was. Partial paralysis had already set

in, and there was no doubt that it was spreading. The bullet
had evidently injured the large artery under the collarbone,
and the weakened part was swelling like a toy balloon. The
blood from Alexander's heart was pumping through it, and
the swollen artery magnified each pulsation. Will shuddered
to think what torture each heartbeat must be, and the
condition would get worse. An operation was imperative.
Will knew that such an operation had not been successful,
the few times it had been tried. He also knew that any decision was entirely up to him. He talked it over with Caroline, letting her quiet confidence in him help to put his
thoughts in order.

"It's been done, Caroline," he said as though thinking
out loud, "ever since the sixteenth century, but always on
small tumors and less vital areas. Fear of the results has prevented men from operating on the subclavian artery. There
is, though, no logical reason why it can't be done in this
case."

"And if it isn't done?" Caroline asked.

The question and answer were in Will's mind. "His left
arm is totally paralyzed already, and the numbness is
spreading. The pain from the heartbeat will become unbearable."

To Will the old Negro was like a wounded animal, suffering in the frightened silence of ignorance. He arranged for
his transfer to Baltimore. The man's trust was complete, and
on the operating table, just before the ether closed his eyes,
he smiled confidingly up at Will. The amphitheater was
filled. Will had carefully explained the operation to his
students, and every head moved instinctively forward as
Will took the scalpel from his assistant. It was the opening
gun in the surgery of main arteries and there was unusual
interest, especially as Dr. Halsted was the star performer.
An incision along the breastbone and another toward the

shoulder permitted Will to turn back the skin. In seconds the huge tumor was exposed—a smooth, dark, shiny bubble between the two normal ends of the artery, several centimeters deep in the neck. It pulsated with every contraction of the heart, and the sound could be heard in the last bench of the otherwise silent amphitheater. It was evident to Will that none of the various aneurysm needles was suitable for the passage of a ligature at this depth, so a narrow, blunt dissector was armed with the finest silk and passed under the artery. By means of this thread and then another, narrow linen tapes were drawn under the subclavian. Both of these were tied with force sufficient to close completely the artery's mouth. The aneurysm became very tense and hard after the ligation, but it was pulseless. The silence in the room was complete. The fateful, dull, monotonous beat of the pulsating tumor was stilled as the blood, prevented from entering the hollow sac, by-passed it silently through other channels. A little silk thread had performed a miracle.

Alexander was returned to his home. Will let him go about his business with the swelling still protruding though infinitely smaller. He wanted to be absolutely sure that the collateral channels were really taking over the blood. Should he cut out the aneurysm before the ends of the artery had become strong enough to resist the blood pressure, there could be only fatal results. When, after two years, Will finally removed the tumor, which had entirely subsided, respect for "Doc" changed to utter devotion.

Meanwhile, during the long winter months in Baltimore, Will continued his classes, his clinics, his constant study, and his experiments. In 1890 he was made full professor, and the trustees of Johns Hopkins finally affirmed their complete faith in him by appointing him Surgeon-in-Chief to the hospital. This was a personal triumph for Will, but somehow he never seemed able to forget Dr. Dalton's descriptions of Civil War surgery. Lister, Koch, aseptic surgery, and the use of cocaine in solution as a local anesthetic had done away with many of the horrors of Civil War days; but there was still tragic suffering, and Will felt that the death rate in many surgical cases was inexcusable. There must be an answer and, although he was becoming acutely conscious of the passing of time, Will was determined to find it.

The answer, Will knew, could not be found in routine operations. He must search for it in those areas where fear and ignorance kept men from experimenting. Two of these areas were inguinal hernia and cancer. Inguinal hernia was the protrusion through the abdominal wall of some organ in the region of the groin. It was a real challenge because there was throughout the profession strong opposition to any radical operation in this region. Even Dr. Bull, Will's old boss at Chambers Street, refused to do more than relieve the patient by removal of the hernial sac. Will disagreed completely with this method. "Imagine," he told his classes, "that you have a hole in the roof of your house and you simply put a piece of canvas over it. Soon the rain comes and pushes the cloth down. You cut off the protruding piece and stitch up what's left of the canvas. When the rains come again, you'll have to do the whole thing over again. You haven't fixed the hole in the roof."

Will studied the history of hernia and found that in ancient Greece a surgeon by the name of Heliodorus performed a very complete operation using crude and painful methods. Following the Greek surgeon's technique, but under anesthesia and the strictest aseptic conditions, Will developed an operation so successful that in 1892, shortly after his fortieth birthday, he was able to stand before a group of surgeons, most of them his seniors in age and experience, and say with supreme confidence, "The time has come when we may operate upon almost every case of hernia not only without danger to the patient but also with almost certain prospect of success." Johns Hopkins Hospital adopted his findings unquestioningly and, as the Hopkins method, Will's operation for inguinal hernia became standard procedure.

Ever since the winter of 1886 when, on his return from the hospital in Providence, he had started work in Dr. Welch's pathological laboratory, Will had interested himself in the field of cancer. One of the most tragic types was breast cancer in women, a condition considered hopeless by surgeons all over the world. The most successful operation was one devised by Will's old friend Dr. Von Volkmann, and even this was successful in only a few cases. When the Johns Hopkins Hospital opened in 1889, Will had been on the point of visiting him in Germany to discuss the operation with him, but the news of Von Volkmann's death reached America that very year. Will realized then that he must go it alone if he were to perfect the operation.

During his years in Welch's laboratory, Will had gathered together a collection of cancerous material taken from patients. He preserved the entire mass—fat, muscle, and all— and carefully labeled it with different-colored ligatures for future study. As far as possible he made a quick study of the material even before removing it at the time of the operation. "A tumor on a plate and one in the breast of a patient— how different!" he would say to his students.

"Cancer," he told them, "was thought of by the ancients as a crab, which accounts for its Latin name. It takes hold of a person, spreads in many directions like the claws of a crab, and cannot be shaken off." He went on to speak of the mistakes in the Von Volkmann method. There had not been enough of the diseased tissue removed. It must, he insisted again and again, be all or nothing. Furthermore, the surgeon's knife must never touch any part that had a cancerous growth. The incision must be around the tumor and only through healthy tissue, and the whole must be removed in one piece.

Will knew that this was radical and had never been done. It was a formidable operation that he proposed, and his courage was put to a severe test—perhaps the most severe of all his experiments. He persisted, and in 1898 he spoke before the American Surgical Association on the results of cancer operations at Johns Hopkins Hospital. He reported that of one hundred and thirty-three cases, fifty-five were still alive with no recurrence, thirty-four were living but had had slight recurrences. A thirteen per cent death rate in a once incurable disease awakened the whole medical world to the fact that here in young Dr. Halsted was a bold pioneer whose methods were fast becoming standard procedure. Breast cancer as a fatal disease became less and less feared.

One day toward the end of summer in 1904 Will received a letter postmarked New Haven, and signed in the name of the President and Fellows of Yale University. They wished, the letter told him, to confer on him the honorary degree of Doctor of Laws, and they hoped that he would honor Yale University by accepting the award at the coming June commencement. He handed the letter to Caroline, who read it and smiled. Words were unnecessary. She knew how much this meant to Will.

On the great day Caroline sat in the audience, listened to the speeches, saw the graduates receive degrees, and waited for the moment that she knew would signalize to Will the culmination of his achievements since leaving Yale as a simple graduate thirty years before. At last the moment came.

"This graduate," a dignified professor in cap and gown began, "of Yale College in the class of 1874, for fifteen years now Professor of Surgery in the Johns Hopkins University, and Surgeon-in-Chief in the Johns Hopkins Hospital won his way to this proud eminence after prolonged studies and practice in the best schools and hospitals in New York and Germany. As teacher, writer, investigator, and operator he has taken an active and distinguished part in the great advancement of the science of surgery during the last two decades. Many of the ablest young surgeons of the country are his ardent disciples. By his ingenuity, skill, and thoroughness, all dominated by the strongest sense of personal responsibility, he has done a great work in the relief of human suffering, and has carried the fame of American surgery throughout the civilized world. Though wars still rage, and men admire the martial conqueror, ours is the loftier delight that lays the victor's wreath upon the brow of him who conquers pain, disease, and deformity—William Stewart Halsted."

Will stood up and received his degree. His eyes scanned the audience . . . met Caroline's, and they rejoiced together. This was indeed the "lee shore."

Chapter

18

HONORS CONTINUED TO COME TO WILL. THE UNIVERSITY OF Edinburgh, the Royal College of Surgeons in England, Columbia College, the Society of Surgeons in France—all bestowed their honorary degrees on him. He accepted them gracefully but, true to his nature, modestly. "Where would I be without all these men who have encouraged me?" he said constantly to Caroline, who smiled but had her own ideas. Will thought back to Henry B. Sands, his first teacher; to Dr. John Dalton, whose study he had shared at the College of Physicians and Surgeons and who had inspired him to an interest in asepsis by his descriptions of Civil War surgery. Then there was the little German doctor, Robert Koch, and the great Richard von Volkmann. He remembered so well the night in Halle when Von Volkmann quoted Wordsworth, and then said, "You have ambition. Never let it go." Almost above them all was Dr. William Welch. Whenever Will received an honor, he murmured a silent prayer of thanks to the man whose constant faith in him had made any success possible.

Von Volkmann and Koch were dead, but Will had made many new friends among the surgeons of France and Germany, such men as Werner Körte, René LeRiche, and Emil Theodor Kocher. He visited them all, worked with them, and watched them operate. It was an international exchange of ideas in surgery, and Will was enthusiastic.

In July, 1914, the German Surgical Association had been meeting in Berlin, and Will was enjoying a brief visit with Professor Körte and his family before leaving for home. There was a tenseness in the air. Goose-stepping soldiers became a common sight. Rumors were everywhere, but in the charming family circle of the Berlin doctor it was hard to believe that anything was amiss. Perhaps there was a silent understanding that rumors should be ignored. The two doctors talked together of surgery; Körte's two daughters had just become engaged, and there was much mutual rejoicing.

Then came the fourth of August. Rumors became realities that could no longer be ignored. England declared war on Germany, and German troops goose-stepped to the Belgian border. Will Halsted was no longer a friendly visiting surgeon. He became a neutral in a country at war, and he soon found that to be a quite different matter. Every citizen of a neutral country who happened to be in Berlin had only one idea in mind—to get home. The trains and the roads to Holland, which was the central gateway out of Germany, were filled with people. Panic was growing. The American Legation at The Hague, under Dr. Henry Van Dyke, tried to cater to everybody, and found itself on a twenty-four-hour merry-go-round.

Will's farewells to the Körte family were brief, but had a very deep significance to him. Somehow he felt that he was saying good-by to all his European colleagues, especially those from Germany and Austria. The air was filled with hate, and there seemed no reason to think that war would ever end. Surgical knowledge was being cut off from one of its greatest sources of inspiration. In the few minutes of farewell, Will promised himself that now, more than ever, he would dedicate himself to carrying on and perfecting all he had learned from the great German surgeons.

The German armies were already besieging Antwerp from the south, but travelers caught in northern Germany were still able to flee, by overcrowded trains, ox carts, or on foot, over the two hundred miles or more to the border of Holland. As a member of the German Surgical Association, and with letters of introduction to many well-known figures, Will was able to move rather freely. However, he was not in the most robust health, and the journey to the border was a definite ordeal.

He was riding in a third-class carriage filled to far more than its capacity. When they stopped on the Dutch side of the border Will got out to stretch, even at the risk of losing his seat. Besides the people fortunate enough to be on a train, hundreds of refugees from the Antwerp region were straggling in frightened flight across the border. Ox carts and makeshift ambulances carried the sick and wounded. One of the carts stopped near Will, and he had a close look at the men sitting and lying on the floor. It was not a nice sight even to Will, used as he was to blood and wounds. Shell splinters had destroyed much of one man's face, and Will was about to turn away in hopeless frustration when someone spoke to him.

"Not as easy to fix as a little dog's rib, Dr. Halsted, but not impossible."

Will looked up in astonishment at hearing his own name in this faraway place. He met the gaze of a tall man, slightly older than himself, familiar to him in only the vaguest and most indefinable way. Before he had a chance to straighten out his thoughts, the stranger spoke again.

"I'm afraid you don't remember me," he went on. "My name is Roger Bacon. I was a medical student at Yale in 1874. We met on a—"

Will interrupted. How many times in his life had he had this vision! "Of course!" he exclaimed. "The dark street and the little dog. I shall never forget it."

The two shook hands, but practical matters prevented any emotional talk. "We'd better get aboard, or we'll stay here forever," Bacon warned, and the two men squeezed into an overflowing compartment.

"What did you mean," Will asked when the train was again in motion, "about something not being impossible?"

"The man on the cart with his face all smashed. It's not really any more hopeless than your little dog and his broken rib," Bacon replied.

Will had seen and performed seeming miracles of surgery, but to put together that shattered face seemed something beyond understanding.

"Let me explain," Bacon went on.

The rattling of the train, the sobbing, the coughing, and the general restlessness of frightened strangers made it hard for Will to follow every detail of Bacon's story. At the end of half an hour he gathered that Bacon had contracted tuberculosis shortly after meeting Will. He had been forced to give up his last year of medical school, and had gone to Davos in Switzerland. There he had recovered his health and, instead of going back to medical school, had decided to make dentistry his career. Being at heart a surgeon, he had taken up dental surgery—the restoring of broken jaws and facial structure that had become injured. Now he was on his way to the American Hospital at Neuilly in France.

Will listened in growing awe as Bacon told him of the miracles of facial surgery. He envied him the opportunity for immediate help to suffering men, but his own duties called him home, and he regretfully said good-by to his newfound friend. In a week he was on his way to America.

From New York he took a train for home. Caroline met

him at the station and drove him to High Hampton. He had
realized the moment he landed in New York that the war
was quite a different thing in America. It was in the head-
lines, in the gossip and rumor of the street, or even out of
mind entirely. He listened to the news of the farm, of his
dahlias and his dogs because he loved them all, but he kept
thinking of the man on the Belgian border with his face
torn apart, and he wanted to do something about it.

He took up his duties at Baltimore. There must be no
letup in his routine work. The training of young surgeons
suddenly became of tremendous importance. Men in faraway Europe were pleading for doctors to cure their
mangled bodies, and these young men filled with Will's
enthusiasm were the ones to bring that help. A unit was
formed and the "Johns Hopkins Boys" joined with other
Americans in volunteering to bring what comfort they could
to the soldiers of a foreign nation. Will wanted to go himself,
but Dr. Welch dissuaded him.

"Face this thing, Will," he said one day. "You're sixty-two
years old and not strong enough to last long over there.
But even if you were, you are far more important here.
Don't forget that you are part of the factory that turns out
these young surgeons. Without you the quality would not be
as good." Dr. Welch always had a way of putting things
in the right light, and Will reluctantly agreed.

Hearing from his French doctor friends of the horrors of
infection and gangrene in wounds, Will stressed more and
more his theories of complete asepsis. One day he received
a batch of photographs from Dr. LeRiche in Paris showing
wounds and the conditions under which they were treated.
He discussed them with his classes and wrote back to Paris
pages of advice and suggestions. These were enthusiastically
received, and Dr. LeRiche wrote a letter of gratitude. "You
will never believe me when I tell you of the depth of the

impression you have made on me. Since my trip in 1913, you have been the master surgeon under whom I should have been happy to work." With Caroline's help Will organized volunteers who made over a million sterile dressings. If he couldn't be there, he told himself, he could at least use his knowledge and skill to help.

The war dragged on for four devastating years. Will's health began failing him; but there was no letup in his activities, except when he was actually confined to bed. Then suddenly in 1918 he recognized symptoms of gallstones, the same trouble for which he had operated on his mother some thirty years before. He felt a sharp, irregular pain in the region of his right hip, at times so severe that he doubled up in an effort to ease it. During one of these attacks Caroline had him taken to the hospital, where one of his own surgeons, Dr. Follis, prepared to operate. In spite of his pain, Will insisted on giving suggestions for the operation. He wanted drainage, he said, through the cystic duct; but due to his condition at the time of the operation, this was impossible and the usual open drainage method was used.

For three weeks Will was in agony as the digestive fluid drained out. Food became utterly distasteful to him, and Caroline and his doctors had to force him to eat. Until the sinus closed and the bile returned to its normal function of helping in the digestion, he lost thirty pounds. The operation, however, appeared to be a success. Will was finally relieved of pain and able to be up and about. He knew that he would never again be really active, but he couldn't actually let go. "I can still think," he said to Caroline one day, "and I can read and write and talk. When I can't do any of those things, it will be time to quit."

Papers on goiter, arteries, aneurysms, and cancer poured from his pen. Occasionally he attended meetings, and very occasionally delivered lectures. Deep down in his own mind he knew there was little more that he could do in his profession. He was proud of the honors that had been heaped upon him, but he was prouder still of any contributions he had made to relieve human suffering.

Then one day in 1922 he received an invitation to attend a dinner to be given by the Maryland Dental Association. He thought at once of his friend Roger Bacon. How thoughtful of him to remember! He accepted with pleasure. To his surprise there was no sign of Roger Bacon and, furthermore, he was seated at the speakers' table next to the toastmaster. The dinner was excellent, and the three hundred or more guests did full justice to it. Then the toastmaster rose. He spoke of the progress of dental knowledge; he lauded the extraordinary accomplishments of the American dental surgeons in the late war in restoring faces apparently irreparably disfigured by shell explosions.

"And now," he continued, "we come to the real purpose of this meeting. We have as a guest tonight one of the great surgeons of our time. The list of those indebted to him who have benefited by his skill, his patience, his courage, and his generosity would be too long to read. I shall speak of only one of the countless groups. The National Dental Association has asked me to represent them in presenting to Dr. William Stewart Halsted this gold medal in recognition of his original researches and discoveries upon which the technique of local and neurological anesthesia in oral and dental practice now rests."

The ovation was a standing one. Will disliked making speeches, and his words of thanks, though sincere and heartfelt, were brief.

"I shall not sleep tonight," he said in closing, "because you have made me too happy. Once before in my life I was kept awake by a great happiness—the night that I passed successfully the examination for Bellevue Hospital in 1876."

When the last guest had left, the chairman turned to Will to say good-by.

"I'm sorry, Dr. Halsted," he said, "that an old friend of yours, Roger Bacon, was unable to be here tonight. He especially asked me to give you this after the dinner." He handed Will a small package. Inside was a well-worn copy of Gray's *Anatomy*, and on the flyleaf was inscribed "To Will Halsted who loves dogs and knows his anatomy," and it was signed "Roger Bacon, D.D.S." Under the signature, Bacon had added, "I have recommended books to hundreds of people, but no one has ever made such good use of them."

He gave Caroline a full account of the dinner, and showed her the copy of Gray's *Anatomy*.

"That was my first experiment," he said with a rather wistful smile, "and I've never regretted making it. "He put the book carefully on a shelf with some of his other rare volumes, and lighted a cigarette. The dinner had been an exciting event, and a happy one; but he was tired.

May, June, and July passed pleasantly enough for Will. He was really glad of a rest, and he even consented to have his photograph taken by the hospital photographer. This was a procedure he had always disliked and avoided; and when he saw the proofs, he remarked laughingly to Caroline, "They all look the way I do when one of my attacks is upon me."

One morning in August he asked Caroline to telegraph to the hospital in Baltimore and have a surgeon ready to operate. "It's my old enemy again, Caroline," he said quietly. She hurried him to the hospital, where everything was in readiness. Everyone on the staff was standing by. The Professor was suffering, and everything must be done to relieve him. On the operating table Will whispered to Dr. Reid, "Be absolutely sure this time that drainage is done through the cystic duct—if there is anything left of it after the last operation. It may be my last experiment." The ether cone covered the faint smile around his mouth.

Dr. Reid's skill was unquestionable. A sizable stone was removed through an incision in the common duct, and the wound perfectly sutured. There was hope for the Professor. His devoted colleagues watched over him night and day. By September he began to weaken. Blood was eagerly given by Dr. Reid and others; but pneumonic fever set in, and on September 7 Will Halsted died. Death, it was determined, had resulted from pneumonia and pleurisy, together with advanced arteriosclerosis. There was no general peritonitis. The drainage through the cystic duct had been perfect. Will's last experiment was a success.

The next day the Baltimore *Sun* carried an editorial:

Because Dr. William S. Halsted lived, the world is a better, a safer, a happier place in which to be. In his death, not only Baltimore, but civilization everywhere has sustained a heavy loss. He was one of the few men who really count. Quiet, simple, unostentatious except in the medical world, where he towered, a great and dominating figure, the full scope of his genius and the tremendous extent and value of his service to mankind were neither generally known nor generally appreciated. To the Johns Hopkins Hospital, the institution to whose reputation and upbuilding he had so enormously contributed, his death is a staggering blow. Along with Osler and Welch he laid the foundation upon which Hopkins so solidly rests today.

BIBLIOGRAPHY

Books

BERNHEIM, BERTRAM M. *Story of Johns Hopkins.* New York and Toronto: Whittlesey House, 1930.

CALDER, RITCHIE. *Medicine and Man.* New York: New American Library, 1958.

CROWE, SAMUEL JAMES. *Halsted of Johns Hopkins.* Springfield: C. C. Thomas, 1957.

FOX, RUTH. *Great Men of Medicine.* New York: Random House, 1947.

HALSTED, WILLIAM STEWART. *Surgical Papers.* Baltimore: Johns Hopkins Press, 1924.

HARLEY, JOHN H. *The Healing Touch.* Springfield: C. C. Thomas, 1951.

MacCULLUM, WILLIAM GEORGE. *William Stewart Halsted, Surgeon.* Baltimore: Johns Hopkins Press, and London: H. Milford, 1930.

POWERS, SIR D'ARCY. *A Mirror for Surgeons.* Boston: Little Brown & Co., 1939.

THORWALD, JURGEN. *The Century of the Surgeon.* New York: Pantheon, 1956.

——————————. *The Triumph of Surgery.* New York: Pantheon, 1957.

TUCKER, AUGUSTA. *Miss Susie Slagle's.* New York: Harper and Bros., 1939.

Periodicals

BLOODGOOD, Joseph C. "Halsted Thirty-Six Years Ago," *American Journal of Surgery,* 1931.

CHESNEY, ALAN M. "Halsted, Hopkins' First Professor of Surgery," *Johns Hopkins Magazine* (Baltimore), February, 1952.

FINNEY, JOHN M. T. "A Personal Appraisal of Dr. Halsted," *Johns Hopkins Bulletin,* 1925.

HEUER, DR. GEORGE. "Dr. Halsted," Supplement to *Johns Hopkins Hospital Bulletin,* February, 1952.

KOCH, ROBERT. "Dr. Koch's Discovery," *North American Review,* CLI (1890).

————. "The Etiology of Anthrax," *Modern Classics* (Baltimore), 1938.

KOLLER, CARL. "Cocaine Finder," *New York Times,* May 24, 1936.

————. "Historical Notes on the Beginning of Local Anaesthesia," *Journal of the American Medical Association* (Chicago), May 2, 1928.

MATAS, RUDOLPH. "William Stewart Halsted," *Archives of Surgery,* January, 1925.

"William Stewart Halsted Centenary," *Surgery* XXXII, No. 1 (1952).

INDEX